SCHOLASTIC
LITERACY SKILLS

Spelling
Years 1-2

TERMS AND CONDITIONS

IMPORTANT – PERMITTED USE AND WARNINGS – READ CAREFULLY BEFORE USING

Minimum system requirements:

- PC or Mac with CD-ROM drive (16x speed recommended) and 512MB RAM
- P4 or G4 processor
- Windows 2000/XP/Vista or Mac OS 10.3 to 10.6

For all technical support queries, please phone Scholastic Customer Services on 0845 6039091.

Author
Sally Gray

Editor
Rachel Mackinnon

Assistant editors
Dodi Beardshaw and Sarah Sodhi

CD-ROM design and development team
Joy Monkhouse, Anna Oliwa,
Micky Pledge, Rebecca Male, Allison Parry,
Shoo Fly Publishing and Haremi

Series designers
Shelley Best and Anna Oliwa

Designer
Sonja Bagley

Illustrations
Cathy Hughes/Beehive Illustration

Designed using Adobe Indesign
Published by Scholastic Ltd, Villiers House,
Clarendon Avenue, Leamington Spa,
Warwickshire CV32 5PR
www.scholastic.co.uk

Printed by Bell & Bain Ltd, Glasgow
Text © 2009 Sally Gray
© 2009 Scholastic Ltd
2 3 4 5 6 7 8 9 0   2 3 4 5 6 7 8

British Library Cataloguing-in-Publication Data
A catalogue record for this book is available from
the British Library.
ISBN 978-1407-10055-5

MIX
Paper from
responsible sources
FSC® C007785

Acknowledgements

The publishers gratefully acknowledge permission to reproduce
the following copyright material:

Sue Palmer for the use of extracts from *Scholastic Literacy Skills:
Phonics Term by Term* by Sue Palmer © 1999, Sue Palmer (1999,
Scholastic).

Every effort has been made to trace copyright holders for the
works reproduced in this book, and the publishers apologise for
any inadvertent omissions.

Extracts from Primary National Strategy's Primary Framework for
Literacy (2006) www.standards.dfes.gov.uk/primaryframework ©
Crown copyright. Reproduced under the terms of the Click Use
Licence.

Extracts from *Letters and Sounds* © Crown copyright. Reproduced
under the terms of the Click Use Licence.

Contents

Chapter 1

Sounds

Chapter 2

Letters

Chapter 3

Digraphs

Chapter 4

Adjacent consonants

Chapter 5

New grapheme representations

Chapter 6

Affixes

Introduction

The Scholastic Literacy Skills: Spelling series

Learning to spell depends on much more than simply memorising words. Exercises, word lists and tests are not enough. Children need to actively engage in the process, tackling new words using knowledge and skills acquired, taking risks and making errors. Purposeful writing is a key to learning to spell. Children need to see spelling as a useful tool for communication (rather than a rod to be beaten with!). To study the spelling of words we need to take them out of context but context is needed to learn how to use them and to give purpose for using them.

This series provides a bank of adaptable ideas and resources for teaching spelling. Each chapter is, to some extent, independent of the others and chapters do not, therefore, always need to be followed in order. Activities within a section sometimes build upon each other and should be followed sequentially. It is anticipated that sections and activities will be selected as required to fit in with medium term planning for each term.

Overview of the teaching of spelling

In English the relationship between sounds and letters (phonics) has been complicated by the complex history of the English language and there is not a simple one-to-one correspondence. Despite this complexity, a great deal of the relationship between letters and sounds is rule-bound, which means phonics works, but not all of the time. There is logic and pattern but there are also 'oddities'.

However spelling does not only represent sound; it also represents grammar and meaning. For example, the '-ed' suffix that identifies regular past-tense verbs can be pronounced /d/ or /id/ or /t/ but never /ed/, but it is always spelled 'ed'. If spelling only represented sound, different accents would require different spellings. Instead of viewing the complexity as a problem, perhaps we might more usefully celebrate the richness and resourcefulness of English spelling.

Teaching spelling involves drawing children's attention to patterns: patterns of sounds and letters, patterns related to grammatical functions and patterns related to word origin. Although English spelling does have 'rules', such as 'q' is always followed by 'u', it is much more realistic to talk about patterns, conventions, possibilities and probabilities. Many so-called rules have so many exceptions or are so complex to explain, that

they are not worth teaching. To teach something as a rule which is later contradicted is not helpful. Children become active, constructive learners by investigating and generalising common patterns, and acknowledging exceptions.

About the product

This book contains seven chapters of activities for teaching spelling. Each chapter focuses on a different aspect of spelling knowledge or skills, and is organised into three sections with clear objectives, background information for the concepts taught, teaching ideas, and photocopiable pages for use in whole class teaching, with groups or for independent work. Each chapter also features a poster and assessment section. The General activities section at the end of the book provides a set of generic games, activities and circle times linked to the activities in this book.

Posters

Each chapter has one poster. These posters are related to the subject of the chapter and should be displayed and used for reference throughout the work on the chapter. The poster notes (on the chapter opening page) offer suggestions for how they could be used. There are black and white versions in the book and full-colour versions on the CD-ROM for you to print out or display on your whiteboard.

Assessment

Each chapter concludes with an assessment section. It summarises the objectives and activities in the section, provides pointers on observation and record keeping and includes one assessment photocopiable page (which is also printable from the CD-ROM with answers, where appropriate).

Activities

Each section contains three to four activities. These activities all take the form of a photocopiable page which is in the book. Each photocopiable page is also included on the CD-ROM for you to display or print out (these pages are also provides with answers where appropriate). Over thirty of the photocopiable pages have linked interactive activities on the CD-ROM. These interactive activities are designed to act as starter activities to the lesson, giving whole-class support on the information being taught. However, they can also work equally well as plenary activities, reviewing the work the children have just completed.

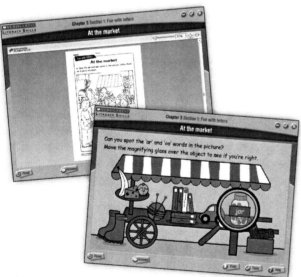

Differentiation

Activities in this book are not differentiated explicitly, although teacher notes may make suggestions for support or extension. Many of the activities can be used with the whole class with extra support provided through differentiated and open-ended questions, use of additional adults, mixed-ability paired or group work or additional input and consolidation before and/or after lessons. Some children may need support with the reading aspects of tasks in order to participate in the spelling objectives.

Using the CD-ROM

Below are brief guidance notes for using the CD-ROM. For more detailed information, see **How to use** on the start-up screen, or **Help** on the relevant screen for information about that page.

The CD-ROM follows the structure of the book and contains:

- All of the photocopiable pages.
- All of the poster pages in full colour.
- Photocopiable pages (with answers where appropriate).
- Over thirty interactive on-screen activities linked to the photocopiable pages.

Getting started

To begin using the CD-ROM, simply place it in your CD- or DVD-ROM drive. Although the CD-ROM should auto-run, if it fails to do so, navigate to the drive and double-click on the red **Start** icon.

Start-up screen

The start-up screen is the first screen that appears. Here you can access: terms and conditions, registration links, how to use the CD-ROM and credits. If you agree to the terms and conditions, click **Start** to continue.

Main menu

The main menu provides links to all of the chapters or all of the resources. Clicking on the relevant **Chapter** icon will take you to the chapter screen where you can access the posters and the chapter's sections. Clicking on **All resources** will take you to a list of all the resources, where you can search by key word or chapter for a specific resource.

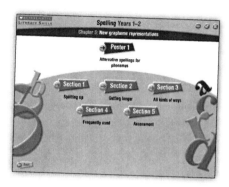

Section screen

Upon choosing a section from the chapter screen, you are taken to a list of resources for that section. Here you can access all of the photocopiable pages related to that section as well as the linked interactive activities.

Resource finder

The **Resource finder** lists all of the resources on the CD-ROM. You can:

- Select a chapter and/or section by selecting the appropriate title from the drop-down menus.
- Search for key words by typing them into the search box.
- Scroll up or down the list of resources to locate the required resource.
- To launch a resource, simply click on its row on the screen.

Navigation

The resources (poster pages, photocopiable pages and interactive activities) all open in separate windows on top of the menu screen. This means that you can have more than one resource open at the same time. To close a resource, click on the **x** in the top right-hand corner of the screen. To return to the menu screen you can either close or minimise a resource.

Closing a resource will not close the program. However, if you are in a menu screen, then clicking on the **x** will close the program. To return to a previous menu screen, you need to click on the **Back** button.

Whiteboard tools

The CD-ROM comes with its own set of whiteboard tools for use on any whiteboard. These include:

- Pen tool
- Highlighter tool
- Eraser
- Sticky note

Click on the **Tools** button at the foot of the screen to access these tools.

Printing

Print the resources by clicking on the **Print** button. The photocopiable pages print as full A4 portrait pages, but please note if you have a landscape photocopiable page or poster you need to set the orientation to landscape in your print preferences. The interactive activities will print what is on the screen. For a full A4 printout you need to set the orientation to landscape in your print preferences.

Top tips

Use these top tips to help your children learn to spell effectively.

In writing encourage children to 'have a go' at spellings to maintain the train of thought and then check later.

Provide plenty of opportunities to hear and enjoy language.

Have fun with language; play with rhymes, alliteration, make a noise, make up voices and sounds

When marking, celebrate what is right and then look for patterns of errors to target teaching.

Encourage use of phonics skills through a range of play-based cross-curricular activities.

Daily practice of grapheme-phoneme correspondences.

Make spelling activities multi-sensory to capitalise on different learning styles.

Provide daily speaking and listening activities that are in tune with the children's interests.

When marking spelling in different curriculum areas, focus on the current spelling rule or convention being taught.

Teach action rhymes, songs and poems; play listening games and memory games in order to develop the range of skills that are needed to become a good speller.

Use individual whiteboards regularly – this enables children to correct mistakes and to use peer support.

Use plastic letters and computers to explore spelling patterns without the physical demands of letter formation.

Develop a range of spelling strategies alongside phonics.

Combine handwriting lessons with spelling to reinforce common letter strings.

Framework objectives

Chapter	Page	Section	Literacy skills objective	Strand 5 (Year 1): Recognise and use alternative ways of spelling the phonemes already taught. Begin to know which words contain which spelling alternatives. Apply phonic knowledge and skills as the prime approach to spelling unfamiliar words that are not completely decodable.	Strand 6 (Year 1): Spell new words using phonics as the prime approach. Segment sounds into their constituent phonemes. Use knowledge of common inflections in spelling. Spell phonically decodable two-and three-syllable words.	Strand 5 (Year 2): Spell with increasing accuracy and confidence, drawing on word recognition and knowledge of word structure and spelling patterns. Spell less common alternative graphemes, including trigraphs.	Strand 6 (Year 2): Spell with increasing accuracy and confidence, drawing on word recognition and knowledge of word structure, and spelling patterns including common inflections and use of double letters. Spell less common alternative graphemes including trigraphs.
Chapter 1	13	Tune in and get to the beat	To tune into sounds, listening and remembering them. To talk about sounds. To recognise rhyming words.	✓	✓		
Chapter 1	18	Playing with sounds	To distinguish between speech sounds. To segment words orally.	✓	✓		
Chapter 2	26	Letters and rhymes	To recognise graphemes and the phonemes they correspond to. To use 'sound talk' to segment words for spelling. To recognise and enjoy rhymes.	✓	✓		
Chapter 2	32	Letters, rhymes and words	To recognise graphemes and the phonemes they correspond to. To use 'sound talk' to segment words for spelling. To recognise and generate rhyming words. To write captions.	✓	✓		
Chapter 3	42	Fun with letters	To learn some new grapheme-phoneme correspondences. To use 'sound talk' and segment words for spelling. To recognise, learn and apply some consonant digraphs and vowel digraphs.	✓	✓		
Chapter 3	48	Word building	To recognise, learn and apply some vowel digraphs. To spell two-syllable and high frequency words. To write labels.	✓	✓		

Framework objectives

Chapter	Page	Section	Literacy skills objective	Strand 5 (Year 1): Recognise and use alternative ways of spelling the phonemes already taught. Begin to know which words contain which spelling alternatives. Apply phonic knowledge and skills as the prime approach to spelling unfamiliar words that are not completely decodable.	Strand 6 (Year 1): Spell new words using phonics as the prime approach. Segment sounds into their constituent phonemes. Use knowledge of common inflections in spelling. Spell phonically decodable two-and three-syllable words.	Strand 5 (Year 2): Spell with increasing accuracy and confidence, drawing on word recognition and knowledge of word structure and spelling patterns. Spell less common alternative graphemes, including trigraphs.	Strand 6 (Year 2): Spell with increasing accuracy and confidence, drawing on word recognition and knowledge of word structure, and spelling patterns including common inflections and use of double letters. Spell less common alternative graphemes including trigraphs.
Chapter 4	60	Combining consonants	To practise previously learned graphemes. To recognise, learn and spell CVC, CVCC and CCVC words.	✓	✓		
Chapter 4	66	Super sentences	To practise previously learned graphemes. To recognise, learn and spell CVC, CVCC and CCVC words. To practise spelling high frequency words and writing sentences.	✓	✓		
Chapter 5	78	Splitting up	To learn about alternative spellings for phonemes. To practise spelling words with a split digraph. To practise spelling words with adjacent consonants.	✓	✓		
Chapter 5	83	Getting longer	To practise spelling words with adjacent consonants. To practise spelling polysyllabic words. To practise writing sentences.	✓	✓		
Chapter 5	88	All kinds of ways	To learn and practise using alternative spellings for phonemes.	✓	✓	✓	✓
Chapter 5	93	Frequently used	To learn and practise using alternative spellings for phonemes. To practise spelling high frequency words.	✓	✓	✓	✓
Chapter 6	102	In the past	To learn about the past tense. To investigate and learn how to add suffixes.	✓	✓	✓	✓
Chapter 6	107	Super suffixes	To investigate and learn how to add suffixes. To investigate how adding suffixes changes words.	✓	✓	✓	✓
Chapter 6	112	All change	To investigate and learn how to add suffixes. To investigate how adding suffixes and prefixes change words.	✓	✓	✓	✓
Chapter 6	117	The long and the short	To investigate how adding suffixes and prefixes change words. To learn how to spell multi-syllable words. To find and learn the difficult bits in words.	✓	✓	✓	✓

Experiment with rhymes

● When teaching spelling to Key Stage 1 children it is important that they experiment and play with language. This can be through rhymes, playground games and chants, stories, poems, songs and so on. This helps the children to spot patterns in language and become more familiar with it.

● The rhyme below is provided for this purpose. It can be used at any point in the book, you could use it to: focus on letter sounds, such as /d/; create some actions to get the children listening to the rhyme; look for rhyming patters and so on.

DIPPY DIPS

Dip, dip, daffodil,
Trumpet shout.
Dip, dip, daffodil,
You are out.

Dip, dip, kangaroo,
Hop about,
Dip, dip, kangaroo,
You are out.

Dip, dip, broccoli,
Swede and sprout,
Dip, dip, broccoli,
You are out.

Dip, dip, elephant,
Grey and stout,
Dip, dip, elephant,
You are out.

Dip, dip, butterfly,
Flap and flit,
Dip, dip, butterfly,
You are it.

Dip, dip, daisy-chain,
Petals all gone,
Dip, dip, daisy-chain,
You are on.

Celia Warren

Chapter 1

Sounds

Introduction

Before the children can move to the learning phonics, and from this begin to make attempts at spelling words, they need to have plenty of practice at playing with sounds and words and had opportunities and hear and discriminate sounds. The chapter focuses on the seven aspects of Phase One of the *Letters and Sounds* programme. By the end of this stage the children will have the opportunity to discriminate and reproduce phonemes and will have been given practice in using 'sound talk' to segment words into phonemes - the first step toward spelling.

In this chapter

Tune in and get to the beat page 13	To tune into sounds, listening and remembering them. To talk about sounds. To recognised rhyming words.
Playing with sounds page 18	To distinguish between speech sounds. To segment words orally.
Assessment page 22	Activities and ideas to assess the ability to find rhyming words.

Poster notes

Voices (page 12)

Use the poster to provide visual clues to help the children experiment with the sounds that their voices can make. Have some fun making 'wheee' sounds for going down a slide, 'sss' sounds for a snake, 'wumph' for banging the door shut and so on. Invite the children to experiment with their own sounds. Then use the poster to make up a sound story together. Tell a story, with the children making the agreed sounds as you point the pictures.

Sounds

Voices

Can you make your voice...

go down a slide?

buzz like a bee?

bark like a dog?

hiss like a snake?

relax on a sofa?

sound surprised?

meow like a cat?

creak like a door?

explode like a firework?

Illustrations © 2009, Cathy Hughes/Beehive Illustration.

Tune in and get to the beat

Objectives

To tune into sounds, listening and remembering them. To talk about sounds. To recognise rhyming words.

Background knowledge

This section depends on good listening. One way to encourage good listening is to set a clear purpose for the activity; whether the children are listening to sounds in the environment, spoken sounds, distinguishing between sounds to describe them or for words that rhyme, providing a focus helps the children engage in the task.

Another important aspect is to have fun with language. Playing games, getting outside and learning new action rhymes, all make the work fun and exciting as well as motivating. By 'doing', the children can feel the language, hear the sounds and feel less inhibited to experiment with making sounds.

As well as listening to sounds and exploring the different ways to make sounds with their bodies, the children need to develop the words required to describe the different actions and noises. Get really descriptive together, using words such as *squelchy*, *crunchy* and *bumpy*, as well as reinforcing words such as *loud*, *quiet*, *fast* and *slow*.

Activities

● **Photocopiable page 14 'Listening walk'**
Before planning a listening walk, make sure that the children understand what is involved in good listening – keeping quiet and still and having ears and eyes ready. Look at an enlarged copy of the photocopiable sheet together. Identify the pictures and ask the children to attempt to make the sounds. Provide a clipboard, the photocopiable sheet and a pencil for each child and go for a walk to see what you can hear.

● **Photocopiable page 15 'Animal sounds game'**
Before you try the activity, discuss the type of sounds that the different animals make. Encourage words such as *squeaky*, *fierce*, *loud*, *deep*, *growly* and so on. Show the children the cards on the photocopiable sheet and invite them to imitate the animals shown, using their voices. Provide instruments that match the ones on the cards and place them in the centre of a circle. Ask each child in turn to choose an animal card and an instrument card that they think will sound like their animal. Let them try using the matching instrument.

● **Photocopiable page 16 'The body beat'**
As a class, spend some time finding out how to make different noises using your bodies, try using your hands, feet, legs and knees, fingers, toes and voices. Describe the sounds you can make and make a list of loud and quiet sounds. Now teach the rhyme, from the photocopiable sheet, to the children, encouraging them to listen to the words and make appropriate actions.

● **Photocopiable page 17 'Rhyming cards'**
Use the cards in a number of ways to develop recognition of rhyming words. For example, put the matching rhyming cards in a bag and invite the children to take turns to pull out a card and say the word. The children check to see if they have an object that rhymes and clap if it does. After each set has been made, say the words together and try to add one or more words to make a rhyming string.

Further ideas

● **Big Book of rhymes:** Make a Big Book of quiet and noisy action rhymes. Divide the book in half, so that when you read the book one way you read all the quite rhymes and, if you turn the book upside down you get all the noisy rhymes, in the other half. You can have two covers to show which side is which.

What's on the CD-ROM

On the CD-ROM you will find:
● Printable versions of all four photocopiable pages.
● Interactive version of 'Rhyming cards'.

Name:

Listening walk

■ What sounds do the things in the pictures make? Listen for them on your walk. Tick the ones you hear.

Notes

_____

_____

_____

_____

_____

Illustrations © 2009, Cathy Hughes/Beehive Illustration.

Name:

Animal sounds game

■ Pick an animal card and an instrument card. Can you make that instrument sound like the animal?

Illustrations © 2009, Cathy Hughes/Beehive Illustration.

Name:

The body beat

■ Read the rhyme and make up some actions.

Come along and join in the band.

You don't need an instrument,

Just lend a hand.

Make a click with your thumb and finger.

Then use your voice,

Like an opera singer.

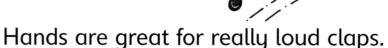

Hands are great for really loud claps.

Knees are useful,

For gentle slaps.

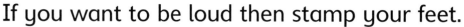

If you want to be loud then stamp your feet.

Drum with your palms,

And get to the beat.

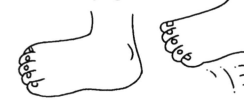

Use your voice for some pops and blows.

Then wiggle your body,

And rap with your toes.

Your body is the best instrument around.

Now show your partner,

Your favourite sound!

Sally Gray

Text © 2009, Sally Gray; Illustrations © 2009, Cathy Hughes/Beehive Illustration.

PHOTOCOPIABLE

■SCHOLASTIC
www.scholastic.co.uk

Tune in and get to the beat

Rhyming cards

■ Cut out the cards. Use them to play rhyming games.

Illustrations © 2009, Cathy Hughes/Beehive Illustration.

Playing with sounds

To distinguish between speech sounds. To segment words orally.

Background knowledge

These activities demand a higher level of auditory discrimination: the ability to detect similarities and differences in sounds. They require the children to reproduce clearly the sounds that they hear. The children will be listening for and saying individual phonemes, and using their voices to experiment with a range of sounds.

In the final activity in this section, 'I-spy', they will be learning how to listen for the order of phonemes in a word. This is done by 'sound talk' – encouraging children to say each sound individually, for example /c/a/t/. Once confident with recognising individual phonemes in a word, they will be encouraged to try to segment words into phonemes themselves.

Activities

● **Photocopiable page 19 'Mum went to market'**
Play this game to develop the children's understanding of alliteration, as well as developing memory skills and vocabulary. Explain that 'Mum' is going to market but can only buy things that begin with the same sound. Tell them that all the things in the list are objects beginning with /b/. Work with a small group and sit in a circle, ask each child, in turn, to pick a card and hold it so that everyone can see. They need to say the sentence: Mum went to market and bought… 'adding their word'. Make it a memory game, with each child repeating the list that went before as well as adding their new word: Mum went to market and bought biscuits, buns and burgers… Play the same game with other letter sounds, perhaps using objects as props.

● **Photocopiable page 20 'Sound story'**
Work with a small group. Cut out the cards from an enlarged copy of the photocopiable sheet. Put the cards in order, and together tell the story. Next, look more closely at the pictures, discuss them and pick out all the things that might be making a sound. Ask for volunteers to use their voices to make the sounds. Finally, tell the story yourself, allocating sound effects to the children in the group (perhaps give one card to each child and ask them to make all the sounds as you refer to them in your story).

● **Photocopiable page 21 'I-spy'**
Cut out the cards and put three in front of you so that the children in your group can see them. Explain that you are going to play a game of I-spy and you are going to use 'sound talk' to sound out one of the cards on display and the rest of the group need to put up their hand and then tell you which card you have spied. For example, I spy a /d/o/g/. Once the children have had a few turns, make it more difficult by putting several cards in front of you and also invite volunteers to be the one to 'sound talk' the clues.

Further ideas

● **Voice opposites:** Together make up voices to suit characters from favourite traditional tales. Have some fun making up inappropriate voices, such as a sweet talking, quiet voice for a troll and a deep growly voice for a princess and so on.

● **Sort the shopping:** Set up a role-play shop and sort the shopping onto different shelves or into bags based on their initial letter sounds.

 What's on the CD-ROM

On the CD-ROM you will find:
● Printable versions of all three photocopiable pages.

Playing with sounds

Mum went to market

■ Cut out the cards for a shopping game.

Illustrations © 2009, Cathy Hughes/Beehive Illustration.

SCHOLASTIC
www.scholastic.co.uk   **PHOTOCOPIABLE**   Scholastic Literacy Skills
Spelling: Years 1 and 2   **19**

Name:

Playing with sounds

Sound story

■ Tell the story. Use your voice to add sound effects.

Illustrations © 2009, Cathy Hughes/Beehive Illustration.

PHOTOCOPIABLE   **■SCHOLASTIC**
www.scholastic.co.uk

Playing with sounds

I-spy

■ Look at the cards and say what they are in 'sound talk'. Use them to play some games.

Illustrations © 2009, Cathy Hughes/Beehive Illustration.

Assessment

Assessment grid

The following grid shows the main objectives and activities covered in this chapter. You can use the grid to locate activities that cover a particular focus that you are keen to monitor.

Objective	Page	Activity title
To tune in to sounds, listening and remembering them.	14 15	Listening walk Animal sounds game
To talk about sounds.	14 15 16	Listening walk Animal sounds game The body beat
To recognise rhyming words.	17	Rhyming cards
To distinguish between speech sounds.	19 20	Mum went to market Sound story
To segment words orally.	21	I-spy

Observation and record keeping

All the children in your group or class will come to you with their own experiences of language. Some will have a wide vocabulary, some may know and recognise all the letters of the alphabet and some will know many of the 44 phonemes in English (according to the International Phonetic Alphabet), whereas others may be learning to speak English as an additional language. It is important to know what stage the children are at to pitch your activities appropriately, and assessment must be an ongoing process. Many of your observations will happen as you and your colleagues work with the children, but it is also important to set up assessment activities in order to get the full picture of a child's knowledge and ability. Early intervention, when problems are spotted, can be vital to later success.

Before you attempt to move children on from oral blending and segmenting you need to be confident that they are able to distinguish between speech sounds and can blend and segment words orally. Recognising rhyming words and being able to generate strings of rhyming words is also a big step forward in preparation for reading and writing.

Assessment activity

● **What you need**
Photocopiable page 23 'Odd one out' (laminated) and counters.
● **What to do**
Work on this activity with individual children. Show the child the laminated card and explain that you would like them to listen to the words as you say them. Say that if they spot any words in each row that rhyme you would like them to put a counter over each rhyming picture. Repeat the activity slowly, row by row. Each time the children identify the rhyming pair, ask them to say the words aloud to check. Praise them for good speaking and listening.

Differentiation

● For less confident learners, listen to the children's pronunciation of each word as you point to the pictures. Note whether there are any sounds (in particular the medial vowel sounds) that are not clear. Say the words as well and exaggerate the rhymes, helping the children to spot them.
● Challenge more confident learners to suggest another one or two rhyming words for each set.

Further learning

● **Nonsense words:** Have fun making up some nonsense words that also rhyme. Share rhyming books together such as *My Cat likes to Hide in Boxes* by Eve Sutton and Lynley Dodd (Puffin Books) and *Pat the Cat* by Colin and Jacqui Hawkins (Pat and Pals Ltd).

Assessment

Odd one out

- Find the pictures that rhyme in each row.

Illustrations © 2009, Cathy Hughes/Beehive Illustration.

Letters

Introduction

This chapter is closely linked to Phase Two of the *Letters and Sounds* programme. It contains activities linked to some of the 19 letters that are recommended to be taught during this phase, as well as activities that reinforce speaking and listening skills and teach rhyming and word building skills. The best way to teach phonics and spelling at this stage is to make the learning a multi-sensory experience using games, rhymes and physical objects. The activities in this chapter all provide scope for this. The chapter finishes with guidelines and suggestions for assessment.

In this chapter

Letters and rhymes page 26	To recognise graphemes and the phonemes they correspond to. To use 'sound talk' to segment words for spelling. To recognise and enjoy rhymes.
Letters, rhymes and words page 32	To recognise graphemes and the phonemes they correspond to. To use 'sound talk' to segment words for spelling. To recognise and generate rhyming words. To write captions.
Assessment page 38	Activities and ideas to assess grapheme-phoneme recognition.

Poster notes

Sound talk (page 25)

Oral blending and segmentation skills require regular practice. Use this poster to encourage the children to 'sound talk' some simple CVC (consonant-vowel-consonant) words. You can simply point to the picture and invite an individual to 'sound talk' what they can see, or you can adapt the poster to suit other activities, such as finding objects beginning with a certain letter or finding an object that rhymes with a word. For example, *Point to a word that rhymes with 'ham'*.

Letters

Sound talk

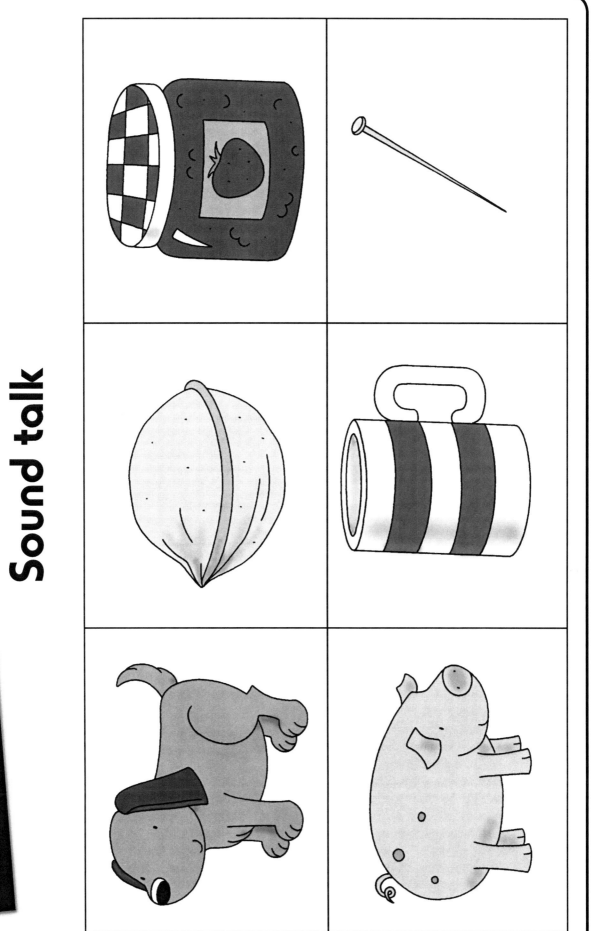

Letters and rhymes

Objectives

To recognise graphemes and the phonemes they correspond to. To use 'sound talk' to segment words for spelling. To recognise and enjoy rhymes.

Background knowledge

Before commencing any activities, decide on the order and frequency with which you will introduce letters to your children (it will vary from child to child). *Letters and Sounds* suggests an order of five sets (one per week) for Phase Two and the activities that follow in this chapter are broadly based upon this order. Teach each grapheme (letter or sequence of letters that represent a phoneme) as a single phoneme first before progressing to word-building activities that combine phonemes. Move on from oral segmenting work (such as 'sound talk') to being able to record the phonemes to spell simple CV (consonant, vowel) and CVC words.

Activities

● **Photocopiable pages 27 and 28 'Letters and pictures'**
Before completing these activities, the children need to have had practice at saying, recognising and writing the letters that represent the phonemes. Read through the instructions on the sheet and together 'sound talk' the letters and the words that represent the objects. Explain how to use lines or arrows to match the letters with objects that begin with the same letter sound.
● **Photocopiable page 29 'Twinkle, twinkle'**
This activity reinforces the use of some of the letters practised in the previous activity. Learning through rhymes and songs is an excellent memory aid for young children and provides a meaningful context for reinforcing letter sounds. Sing the song several times and, orally, practise missing out words for the children to supply before asking them to record on the page.

● **Photocopiable page 30 'Make some words'**
Phoneme frames help children to segment words. This photocopiable sheet provides a two- and three-square phoneme frame for some word-building activities, as well as a selection of letters. Provide each child or pair with a photocopiable sheet and ask them to cut out the phonemes and to make the words that you specify, or allow them to build words of their choice.
● **Photocopiable page 31 'In the tin'**
This activity uses the majority of the letters from sets one to three of Phase Two of *Letters and Sounds*. Copy the photocopiable sheet onto card. Working with a group, ask the children to match the words to the pictures. Cut out the words and pictures and use them to play a circle game. Sit the children in a circle. Turn the cards face down in the centre and place a tin next to them. Invite one child at a time to pick up a card and 'sound talk' the word. Say the word as a group and put it in the tin.

Further ideas

● **Cheeky monkey:** Make a small collection of different soft toys that can be used for 'sound talk' activities. Develop their characters to make the phonics work fun; for example, you might have a shy tortoise who speaks very slowly or a cheeky monkey that likes to tell jokes and so on.
● **Poster peeking:** Put sticky notes over each picture on poster page 25 'Sound talk' and write the word that corresponds to the picture on each one. With the children, segment each word and say it together before revealing the hidden picture.

What's on the CD-ROM

On the CD-ROM you will find:
● Printable versions of all five photocopiable pages.
● Answers to 'Letters and pictures (1) and (2)' and 'Twinkle, twinkle'.
● Interactive versions of 'Letters and pictures (1)', 'Twinkle, twinkle', 'Make some words' and 'In the tin'.

Letters and rhymes

Letters and pictures (1)

- Draw arrows to match the pictures with the letters.
- Pick a letter and draw another picture to go with it.

s

a

t

p

Name:

Letters and rhymes

Letters and pictures (2)

- Draw arrows to match the pictures with the letters.
- Pick a letter and draw another picture to go with it.

n

m

d

i

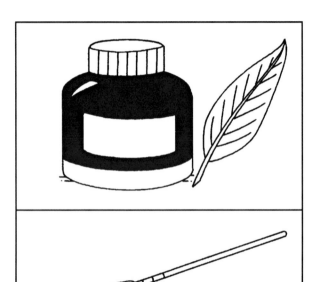

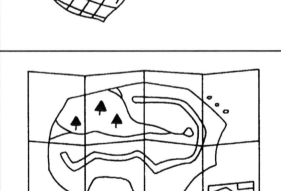

Letters and rhymes

Twinkle, twinkle

■ Read the rhyme below. Then fill in the missing words. Sing the song to the tune of 'Twinkle, Twinkle Little Star'.

Twinkle, twinkle, little pin

Twinkle, twinkle, little pin,

Sharp and shiny, long and thin!

I can put you in a tin,

I can give the tin a spin –

Twinkle, twinkle, little pin,

In a tin you make a din!

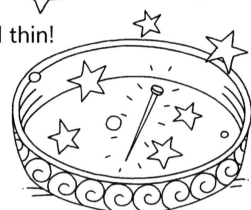

Twinkle, twinkle, little _____ ,

Sharp and shiny, long and _____ !

I can put you in a _____ ,

I can give the _____ a spin –

Twinkle, twinkle, little _____ ,

In a tin you make a _____ !

Sue Palmer

Text © 1999, Sue Palmer; Illustrations © 2009, Cathy Hughes/Beehive Illustration.

Name:

Letters and rhymes

Make some words

■ Cut out the letter cards and use them to make words in the phoneme frames.

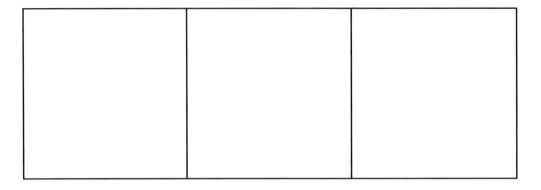

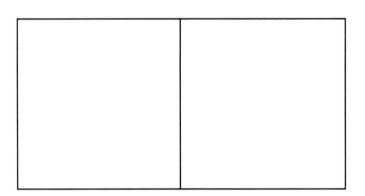

✂

s	a	t	p	i
n	m	d	g	o
	c	k	ck	

■SCHOLASTIC
www.scholastic.co.uk

Letters and rhymes

In the tin

■ Cut out the words and pictures. Match the words to the pictures. Use the pictures to play a game.

pan	
dog	man
pig	
cap	cat

Illustrations © 2009, Cathy Hughes/Beehive Illustration.

Letters, rhymes and words

Objectives

To recognise graphemes and the phonemes they correspond to. To use 'sound talk' to segment words for spelling. To recognise and generate rhyming words. To write captions.

Background knowledge

Throughout this phase the children will need plenty of practice to recall letters quickly and to correspond graphemes to phonemes. They need help to move on from being able to segment a word orally to spell it, to being able to select letters to represent the phonemes to spell a word. Oral work still plays an important role, particularly as new letters are introduced. Playing games and following recognised formats, such as using 'sound talk' games and word ladders, gives the children confidence to try out their new skills and knowledge.

Activities

● **Photocopiable pages 33 and 36 'Word ladders'**
The aim of these games is to change one letter at a time to create a new word, trying to get back to the original word again (though this is optional – it is easier simply to make new words). Before the children try the activities, make sure that they are familiar with the letters (and their phonemes) on the sheet. 'Sound talk' the first word together and experiment with changing the beginning, middle and end letters. Show the children how to add a chosen word to the ladder to start them off.

● **Photocopiable page 34 'In the sack'**
Play a version of this game as a circle game before giving each child a copy of the photocopiable sheet. Provide a sack and a set of objects (similar to the ones illustrated on the photocopiable sheet) and place them in the centre of a circle. Invite one child at a time to place an object that contains the /ck/ phoneme into the sack. Ask them to 'sound talk' the word before they put it in.

● **Photocopiable page 35 'Meet the -at family!'**
Give each child in the group a photocopiable sheet and take it in turns to 'sound talk' the words that match the pictures. Use magnetic letters and whiteboards to make each word after it has been said. Then ask the children to write the words under the pictures on the page.

● **Photocopiable page 37 'Captions'**
Writing captions, using words based on the phonemes learned as well as some tricky high frequency words, is a good way to develop confidence in writing and spelling. Talk about each picture before expecting the children to write. Practise making some of the words using 'sound talk' along with magnetic letters or an interactive whiteboard programme that allows the children to drag and drop letters to make words.

Further ideas

● **Letter and word snap:** Being able to quickly recognise letters and words is a vital skill for reading and spelling success. Use two sets of laminated letter cards or two sets of cards containing the decodable high frequency words to play games of snap.

● **Feely sounds:** Fill a feely bag with CVC objects beginning with your focus letters. Invite individuals to come and feel an object and then either 'sound-talk' it for the others to guess, or give its initial sound plus a clue for them to decipher.

What's on the CD-ROM

On the CD-ROM you will find:
● Printable versions of all five photocopiable pages.
● Answers to 'In the sack' and 'Meet the -at family'
● Interactive versions of 'Word ladders (1)' and 'In the sack'.

Word ladders (1)

- 'Sound talk' the word below. Change one letter at a time to make a new word using the letters in the list.
- Try to return to the first word again.

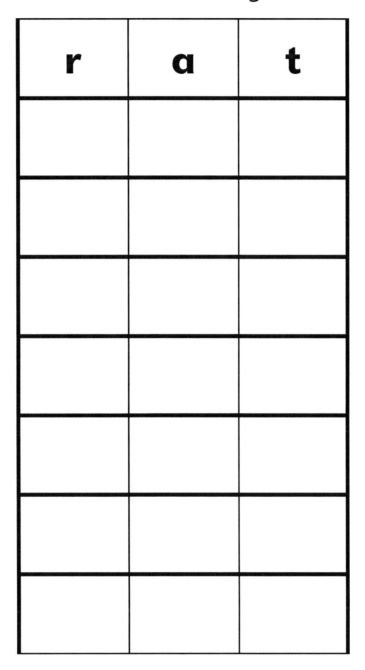

r	a	t

r	l	p	g	t	e	a

Name:

In the sack

- Look at the pictures and 'sound talk' the words.
- Draw arrows to put the **ck** objects into the sack.

PHOTOCOPIABLE

Illustrations © 2009, Cathy Hughes/Beehive Illustration.

Letters, rhymes and words

Meet the -at family!

■ Write the words that match the pictures.

a t

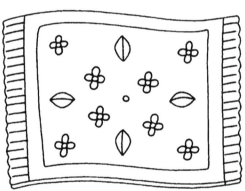

■ Draw a picture to go with the caption.

A cat and a big fat rat.

Name:

Word ladders (2)

■ 'Sound talk' the word below. Change one letter at a time to make a new word using the letters in the list.

■ Try to return to the first word again.

r	u	n

r	s	b	u	i	n

Captions

■ Write a caption to go with each picture.

_____

_____

_____

_____

Illustrations © 2009, Cathy Hughes/Beehive Illustration.

Assessment

Assessment grid

The following grid shows the main objectives and activities covered in this chapter. You can use the grid to locate activities that cover a particular focus that you are keen to monitor.

Objective	Page	Activity title
To recognise graphemes and the phonemes they correspond to.	27 28 34	Letters and pictures (1) Letters and pictures (2) In the sack
To use 'sound talk' to segment words for spelling.	30 31 34	Make some words In the tin In the sack
To recognise and enjoy rhymes.	29	Twinkle, twinkle
To recognise and generate rhyming words.	35	Meet the -at family!
To begin to use segmentation to spell words.	31 33 36	Make some words In the tin Word ladders
To write captions.	37	Captions

Observation and record keeping

It is difficult to sufficiently monitor children when they are taking part in group activities. Individual assessments need to be done on a regular basis to check the children's knowledge of letters and their ability to segment words for spelling. Some children may have a good grasp of grapheme-phoneme correspondences but may lack the capacity to form their letters correctly. For these children it is more appropriate to continue using magnetic letters and letter cards, fans and tiles. As well as formal assessments it is often useful to have a ready supply of sticky notes, scraps of paper or notebooks for jotting down things that you or another adult has noticed. For regular phonics sessions it is worth keeping a record of your successes and things that did not go to plan for future reference.

Assessment activity

● **What you need**
Two copies of photocopiable page 39 'What sound do I make?' (laminated on card, if possible), pencil or pointer, drywipe marker pen and cloth.

● **What to do**
The letters on the photocopiable sheet are the suggested letter sets for Phase Two of *Letters and Sounds*. Display the photocopiable sheet and, with individual children, point to one letter at a time. Ask the child to say the sound of the letter that you point to. Keep a record of the phonemes that they know on your own laminated copy of the sheet by ticking them as they get them. You can transfer this information to your records later (or alternatively use a sheet per child and tick them off and use these as your record).

Differentiation

● For children requiring support, provide a pictorial alphabet frieze and ask them to find the letter on the frieze that matches the one you are pointing to. The picture that they see on the frieze should give them a clue as to the sound it makes.

● For more confident learners, inverse the process and check to see if the child can identify the letter on the photocopiable sheet when you make the letter sound.

Further learning

● **Words and letters:** Invite the children to think of words that start or contain specified letters. Use the letters to make and spell some CVC words.

What sound do I make?

■ Look at the cards and say the sounds.

s	a	t	p
i	n	m	d
g	o	c	k
ck	e	u	r
h	b	f	ff
l	ll	ss	

Chapter 3

Digraphs

Introduction

This chapter introduces vowel and consonant digraphs (phonemes which are represented by two vowels or consonants). It supports the learning of some of the new graphemes that the children are expected to know in Phase Three of *Letters and Sounds*. There are also activities and resources provided to support the learning of two-syllable and high frequency words using the graphemes learned so far. The final two pages of this chapter contain an assessment activity and assessment ideas.

In this chapter

Fun with letters page 42	To learn some new grapheme-phoneme correspondences. To use 'sound talk' and segment words for spelling. To recognise, learn and apply some consonant digraphs and vowel digraphs.
Word building page 48	To recognise, learn and apply some vowel digraphs. To spell two-syllable and high frequency words. To write labels.
Assessment page 56	Activities and ideas to assess spelling using phoneme-grapheme knowledge.

Poster notes

The farmyard (page 41)

The farmyard poster is a bright and appealing picture that can be used alongside many of the activities in this chapter. Within the poster are objects that begin with the newly learned graphemes and phonemes, as well as several two-syllable words. You can use the poster as part of a starter activity to stimulate discussion about rhyming words or a particular phoneme; or it can be used in a plenary session to reinforce the graphemes and phonemes that you have introduced during the main part of a lesson. Ideas for using the poster include asking the children to provide captions and labels for the objects in the farmyard as well as making word lists of objects found. Alternatively you can focus on a phoneme and ask the children to find an example or two of it (such as /oa/ – *goat* and *coat*).

Digraphs

The farmyard

Fun with letters

To learn some new grapheme-phoneme correspondences. To use 'sound talk' and segment words for spelling. To recognise, learn and apply some consonant digraphs and vowel digraphs.

Background knowledge

Grapheme-phoneme correspondence is a vital skill in learning to spell. Knowing that a sound is represented by certain letters will enable children to make an educated guess about how a word may be spelled.

The activities in this section pick out some correspondences that the children will be expected to know at this stage. At this time, the children are only expected to learn one representation of a phoneme. For example, the phoneme /ai/ is represented by the grapheme 'ai' at this stage; later on the children will learn that it can also be represented by 'ay' and 'a–e'.

Activities at this stage should provide a mix of formal phonics teaching and motivating games, rhymes and circle times.

Activities

● **Photocopiable page 43 'Sort the pictures'**
Before completing this activity, the children need to have had practice at saying, recognising and writing the letters that represent the phonemes. Read through the instructions and together 'sound talk' the letters and the words that represent the objects.

● **Photocopiable page 44 'Buzz, quack and yell!'**
This is a fun and noisy game to play with small groups. Before you begin, make sure that the children have had practice at saying, recognising and writing the letters that represent the phonemes. Cut out the cards from the photocopiable sheet and place them face down. Explain that the children must yell, buzz or quack as each word is turned face up. Finish by 'sound talking' each word and putting it into a phoneme frame (see photocopiable page 30 'Make some words') before covering it up, spelling it and checking it.

● **Photocopiable page 45 'sh or ch?'**
Introduce the activity with a circle game where the children chant 'sh' or 'ch' and then take it in turns to say a 'sh' or 'ch' word as you go around the circle. Provide each child with a copy of the photocopiable sheet and ask them to fill in the gaps with 'sh' or 'ch' as appropriate.

● **Photocopiable page 46 'Rhyming fun'**
Work with a small group of children and give each child a photocopiable sheet. Remind the children of the phonemes that the graphemes 'oa', 'ee' and 'igh' represent. Explain that the pictures are missing a rhyming caption which describes what is happening. Together, decide what the captions could be. Invite the children to write the caption (or scribe for those who need support). Challenge them to match the caption to the corresponding grapheme by drawing an arrow.

● **Photocopiable page 47 'At the market'**
Display an enlarged version of the photocopiable sheet and talk about the scene together. Invite the children to spot and have a go at spelling the 'ar' and 'oo' words. Give each child a photocopiable sheet and suggest that they use two colours to colour the set of 'oo' objects and the set of 'ar' objects.

Further ideas

● **Hunt the grapheme:** Focus on a particular grapheme and ask the children to work with a partner to hunt through their reading books to find some examples of it. Ask them to make a list of the words they find.

● **Poem pondering:** Look at some simple poems and find the rhyming words. Talk about the bits of the words that make them rhyme (such as 'oa' in *goat* and *coat*).

 **What's on the CD-ROM**

On the CD-ROM you will find:
● Printable versions of all five photocopiable pages.
● Answers to 'Sort the pictures', 'sh or ch?', 'Rhyming fun' and 'At the market'.
● Interactive versions of all five photocopiable pages.

Fun with letters

Sort the pictures

■ Draw arrows from the pictures to the letters that they start with.

j **v** **w**

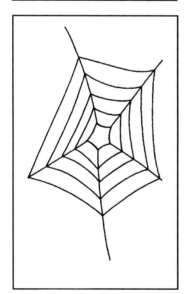  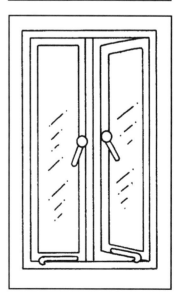

Name:

Fun with letters

Buzz, quack and yell!

■ Cut out the words and lay them face down. Turn them over. Say **buzz** if it contains a **z** or **zz**. Say **quack** if it contains a **qu** and **yell** if it contains a **y**!
■ Next look at each word carefully. Say it in 'sound talk', cover it, spell it and check!

yell	**yes**	**yap**
buzz	**zip**	**zig-zag**
quack	**quit**	**quick**

Fun with letters

sh or ch?

■ Fill in the gaps with **sh** or **ch** to make the words.

_ _ i p

_ _ o p

_ _ i p s

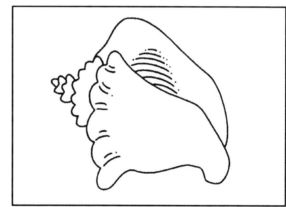

_ _ e l l

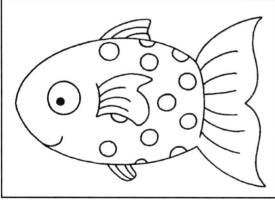

f i _ _

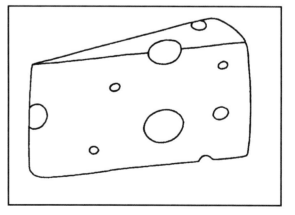

_ _ e e s e

Illustrations © 2009, Cathy Hughes/Beehive Illustration.

SCHOLASTIC
www.scholastic.co.uk   **PHOTOCOPIABLE**   **Scholastic Literacy Skills**
Spelling: Years 1 and 2   **45**

Name:

Fun with letters

Rhyming fun

- ■ Write a rhyming caption underneath each picture.
- ■ Draw arrows to match the captions to the sound.

oa

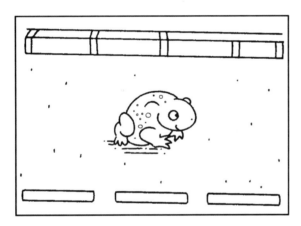

igh

oa

Illustrations © 2009, Cathy Hughes/Beehive Illustration.

PHOTOCOPIABLE

Fun with letters

At the market

■ Spot the **ar** and **oo** words in the picture. Write them on a piece of paper.

Illustrations © 2009, Cathy Hughes/Beehive Illustration.

■SCHOLASTIC
www.scholastic.co.uk   **PHOTOCOPIABLE**   Scholastic Literacy Skills
                                                      Spelling: Years 1 and 2   **47**

Word building

To recognise, learn and apply some vowel digraphs. To spell two-syllable and high frequency words. To write labels.

Background knowledge

Throughout this section the emphasis is on learning the new grapheme-phoneme correspondences as well as stepping up to segmenting and spelling a wider range of CVC words, two-syllable words and learning some further tricky high frequency words. Many of the activities encourage word-building and using spelling patterns to generate new words. To motivate children at this stage it is important to have fun with phonics and spelling; lots of rhymes, songs and alphabet chants are essential, as are activities that use silly sentences, integrating spelling into role-play activities and playing games such as using letter dice.

Activities

● **Photocopiable page 49 'Fill in the gaps'**
With a small group, provide each child with a photocopiable sheet. Read the sentences together and discuss what the missing word might be. Repeat each missing word carefully and ask the children to decide whether it is an 'igh', 'ar' or 'oa' word. Then ask them to filling in the missing word in the space. Think of some more words that contain those sounds.

● **Photocopiable page 50 'Down in the town'**
Hand out the photocopiable sheet and ask the children to complete it individually or in pairs. After completing this activity, play a circle game using some of the new words. As you go around the circle, ask each child to say something they have seen or done *down in the town*.

● **Photocopiable page 51 'Letter dice'**
Play this game in a group. Make the dice and invite the children to throw it in turn. Using the initial sound shown on the dice, they need to add it to either the

grapheme 'ear' or 'air'. At this stage children are only expected to know one pronunciation of the grapheme 'ear', but they may discover that the words *pair* and *pear* sound the same but are spelled differently and have different meanings.

● **Photocopiable page 52 'The tool shop'**
Work with a group and discuss what the pictures show. Decide on the appropriate words to label the pictures. 'Sound talk' them as a group and then invite individuals to try writing a label each. Invite the children to cut out and play freely with the labels, pictures and props to set up a tool shop in your role-play area.

● **Photocopiable page 53 'Clap the words'**
Clapping words with more than one syllable helps children to stretch the word out, hearing the distinct phonemes. 'Sound talk' the words before asking the children to cover them up and spell them on the back of the sheet.

● **Photocopiable pages 54 and 55 'High frequency words'**
Use these flashcards to help the children learn the decodable and tricky high frequency words expected of them during Phase Three of *Letters and Sounds*. Ideas include making two sets of cards to play snap with or matching a set of cards with the words on the photocopiable sheet.

Further ideas

● **Picture box:** Provide a box full of interesting pictures and photographs that the children could easily write labels and captions for.
● **Post boxes:** Provide cards with words that target the graphemes you are working on, such as 'oa', 'er' and 'oo'. Make post boxes each with a label with a grapheme on it. Ask the children to sort the words into groups and post them into the appropriate boxes.

 ### What's on the CD-ROM

On the CD-ROM you will find:
● Printable versions of all seven photocopiable pages.
● Answers to 'Fill in the gaps', 'Down in the town' and 'The tool shop'.

Word building

Fill in the gaps

■ Fill in the gaps in these sentences using **igh**, **ar** and **oa** words.

Turn on the _____ .

I go to the shops in my _____ .

My dog has got a loud _____ .

The moon comes out at _____ .

I wear a hat and _____
when it is cold.

You should wash your
hands with _____ .

SCHOLASTIC
www.scholastic.co.uk   **PHOTOCOPIABLE**   Scholastic Literacy Skills
Spelling: Years 1 and 2   **49**

Name:

Word building

Down in the town

■ Read the sentence below out loud. Listen for the **ow**, **ear** and **air** words. Underline them and write them in the boxes below.

Down in the town I can see an owl with big ears, a cow with a beard and a girl with fair hair.

■ Write some more **ow**, **ear** and **air** words in the boxes. Can you make a sentence with some of them?

ow	ear	air

Word building

Letter dice

- Cut out the shape below. Glue it together to make a letter dice.
- Throw the dice and make some **ear** and **air** words.

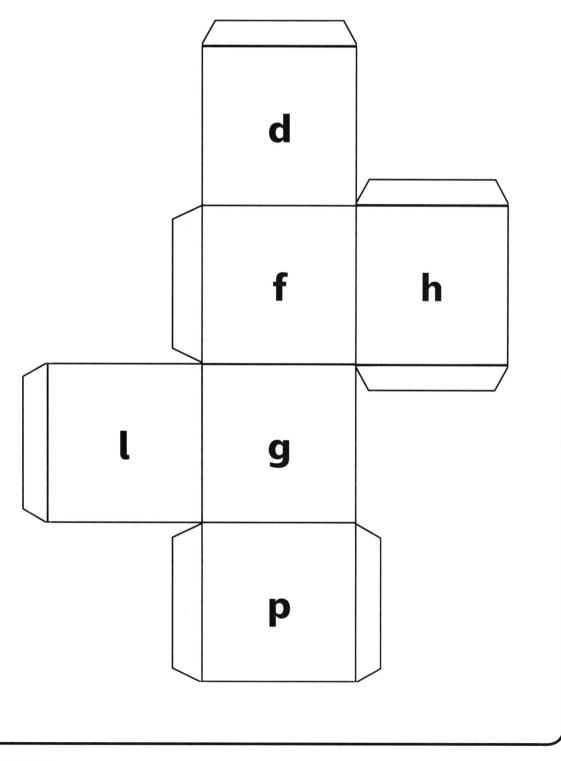

Name:

Word building

The tool shop

■ Label the pictures. Use the pictures to play tool shops.

PHOTOCOPIABLE

SCHOLASTIC
www.scholastic.co.uk

Word building

Clap the words

■ Clap these words. 'Sound talk' each syllable. Cover a word at a time and write it out.

tonight

boatman

rooftop

market

farmyard

cornet

turnip

poison

Illustrations © 2009, Cathy Hughes/Beehive Illustration.

Word building

High frequency words (1)

■ Cut out these flashcards and use them to practise these high frequency words.

will	that
this	**then**
them	**with**
see	**for**
now	**down**
look	**too**

Word building

High frequency words (2)

■ Cut out these flashcards and use them to practise these high frequency words.

he	she
we	me
be	was
you	they
all	are
my	her

Assessment

Assessment grid

The following grid shows the main objectives and activities covered in this chapter. You can use the grid to locate activities that cover a particular focus that you are keen to monitor.

Objective	Page	Activity title
To learn some new grapheme-phoneme correspondences.	43 44	Sort the pictures Buzz, quack and yell!
To use 'sound talk' and segment words for spelling.	44	Buzz, quack and yell!
To recognise, learn and apply some consonant digraphs and vowel digraphs.	45 46 47 49 52 51	sh or ch? Rhyming fun At the market Fill in the gaps Down in the town Letter dice
To spell two-syllable and high frequency words.	52 53 54 55	The tool shop Clap the words High frequency words (1) High frequency words (2)
To write labels.	52	The tool shop

Observation and record keeping

By this stage, the children will be beginning to have better pencil control and most will be able to form the letters correctly during handwriting activities. When concentrating on spelling it may still be useful to allow the children to manipulate magnetic letters or cards so that they are focused on the content rather than the process of their writing.

At this stage the children will be encountering many new graphemes and it is a big step up to realise that some sounds are made up of more than one letter. They will need plenty of practice at listening for sounds and matching them to the graphemes and giving the sound that goes with a grapheme. It is useful to develop a checklist of the new grapheme-phoneme correspondences you are introducing to keep track of individual children's progress and to highlight areas that need further reinforcement.

Assessment activity

● **What you need**

Photocopiable page 57 'Write the words', writing materials and scissors.

● **What to do**

Cut out the picture cards from the photocopiable sheet and make a pile of them, face down on a table. Ask a child to pick a card and then 'sound talk' it without showing you the picture. Can you guess the word? Make a note of the child's ability to segment the word and their pronunciation of the phonemes that make up the word. Continue in this way before giving the child the cards and asking them to write the letters that make up the words in the spaces provided. Observe whether they can represent the phonemes they have articulated with the appropriate graphemes.

Differentiation

● For children requiring support, decide how much of the word you are going to ask them to provide – perhaps they are only ready to supply the initial phoneme.

● For each word, ask more confident learners to think of at least one word that rhymes. Ask the child to write the rhyming words on the back of the card.

Further learning

● **Captions:** Put the words into captions or short sentences and invite the children to try writing these. Make word banks of rhyming CVC words together.

Assessment

Write the words

■ Write the words that match the pictures.

Illustrations © 2009, Cathy Hughes/Beehive Illustration.

Chapter 4
Adjacent consonants

Introduction

This chapter supports the learning of segmenting and spelling words with adjacent consonants and provides opportunities to practise the graphemes that the children have already learned. The activities are in line with some of the words and consonant clusters found in Phase Four of *Letters and Sounds*. There are also activities and resources provided to support the learning of polysyllabic and high frequency words using the 42 phonemes already encountered. The final two pages of this chapter contain an assessment activity and ideas for assessment.

In this chapter

Combining consonants page 60	To practise previously learned graphemes. To recognise, learn and spell CVC, CVCC and CCVC words.
Super sentences page 66	To practise previously learned graphemes. To recognise, learn and spell CVC, CVCC and CCVC words. To practise spelling high frequency words and writing sentences.
Assessment page 74	Activities and ideas to assess understanding and spelling of words with adjacent consonants.

Poster notes

Rhyming words (page 59)
The poster shows five groups of CCVC rhyming words. It can be used to teach and reinforce knowledge of common word families and also to practise blending and segmenting words with initial consonant clusters. Develop visual strategies by asking the children to find the words with the same initial consonant cluster. Investigate changing the initial consonant(s) to generate new words. Use the poster to play games, such as writing the beginnings of the words and inviting children to decide on consonants that will make words or altering one of the words in each group to create a nonsense word and asking the children to spot which word is not correct.

Adjacent consonants

Rhyming words

clip	drip	skip	slip
drop	crop	flop	stop
slap	clap	flap	trap
drag	flag	snag	stag
plum	drum	glum	slum

Illustrations © 2009, Cathy Hughes/Beehive Illustration.

Combining consonants

To practise previously learned graphemes. To recognise, learn and spell CVC, CVCC and CCVC words.

Background knowledge

The activities in this section use a lot of rhyming games and words to pick out spelling patterns and to help the children to blend and subsequently segment words with adjacent consonants. 'Sound talking' words is still an important strategy for breaking down words into their constituent phonemes. Reinforcement of the 42 phonemes that will have been learned by this stage is essential and will require plenty of practice.

Many of the activities in this section can be reapplied using different letters, rhymes and consonant clusters. For example, the letter and rhyme spinners can be adapted by fixing sticky labels on top of the words or letters. At this stage, time spent singing and chanting rhymes, playing games and having fun with language is still a motivating and beneficial way to approach phonics and spelling.

Activities

● **Photocopiable page 61 'Rhyming partners'**
Practice in recognising rhymes and playing rhyming games helps children to listen for phonemes and to identify common letter strings in words. As a follow-up, ask the children to remember and write some of the word endings (such as '-ump' and '-amp') on individual whiteboards. Try placing different letters in front to make some real and nonsense words.

● **Photocopiable pages 62 and 63 'Add a letter'**
Children enjoy making new words from existing ones – it helps to develop visual strategies for spelling, enabling them to spot common patterns of graphemes to build up word families. Say the existing word before

'sound talking' the new word with the extra letter. Encourage the children to verbalise and write some sentences to go with the new words, to check their understanding of the vocabulary. Refer to the poster for some other examples of word families.

● **Photocopiable page 64 'Spin a letter'**
Copy the photocopiable sheet onto card and fix the arrow into place with a split pin. Use this as a versatile resource for favourite spelling games and activities. Ideas include spinning and making a word list of words beginning, containing or ending with that letter; spinning several times and making real or nonsense words; adding the letter to an existing word to make a new word (see photocopiable pages 62 and 63 'Add a letter'). The spinner can be adapted by sticking labels with different graphemes or phonemes over the top.

● **Photocopiable page 65 'Word family spinner'**
Copy the photocopiable sheet onto card and fix the arrow spinner in place. Use this as a versatile resource for favourite spelling games and activities, for example: spin and think of rhyming words; spin, look, cover, write and check; spin or focus on the consonant cluster, writing a list of words that also begin with that cluster.

Further ideas

● **Favourite songs:** Look for rhyming words in simple poems and favourite songs. Display the poems and songs and look for the word patterns in the rhymes.
● **Class cuddly:** Introduce a cuddly toy that mixes up words and sounds for the children to help.

What's on the CD-ROM

On the CD-ROM you will find:
● Printable versions of all five photocopiable pages.
● Answers to 'Rhyming partners', 'Add a letter (1) and (2)'.
● Interactive versions of 'Rhyming partners' and 'Add a letter (1)'.

Combining consonants

Rhyming partners

■ Match the words from the bottom of the page with words that rhyme from the top.

■ Write them under the rhyming word. Then add some more of your own.

jump	**lamp**	**band**
_____	_____	_____
_____	_____	_____
_____	_____	_____

best	**gust**
_____	_____
_____	_____
_____	_____

test	sand	camp	bust	hump

■SCHOLASTIC
www.scholastic.co.uk   **PHOTOCOPIABLE**   Scholastic Literacy Skills
Spelling: Years 1 and 2   **61**

Name:

Add a letter (1)

■ Read the words below. Add an **s** or a **t** at the beginning to make different words.

_____ pot   _____ peck   _____ top

_____ rip   _____ rack   _____ win

■ Write some sentences using the new words.

_____

_____

_____

_____

_____

Illustrations © 2009, Cathy Hughes/Beehive Illustration.

PHOTOCOPIABLE

Add a letter (2)

■ Read the words below. Now add a **c**, **p** or **g** at the beginning to make different words.

_____ ink   _____ lad   _____ ran

_____ rip   _____ lap

■ Write some sentences using the new words.

_____

_____

_____

_____

_____

Illustrations © 2009, Cathy Hughes/Beehive Illustration.

Name:

Spin a letter

■ Cut out the spinner and arrow below. Attach the arrow to the spinner with a split pin in the centre.

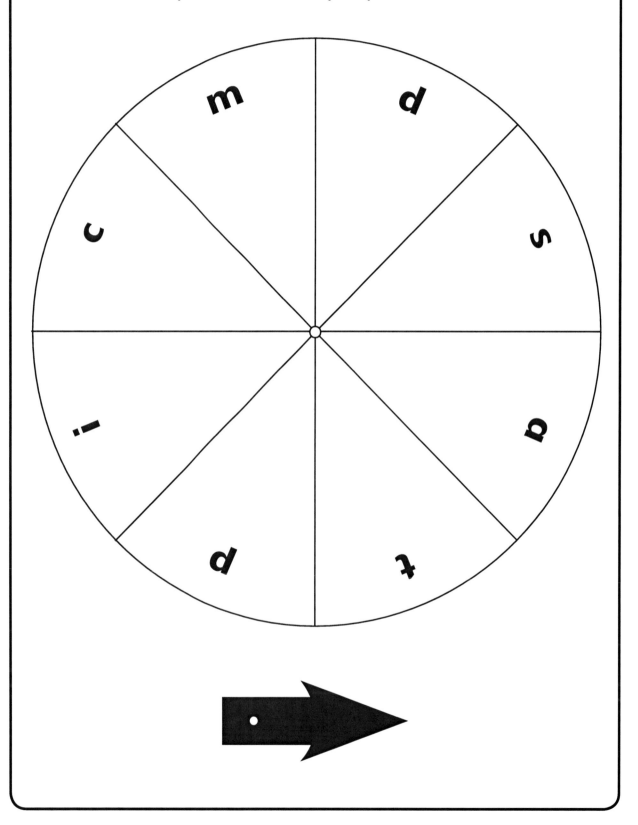

PHOTOCOPIABLE

Word family spinner

■ Cut out the spinner and arrow below. Attach the arrow to the spinner with a split pin in the centre.

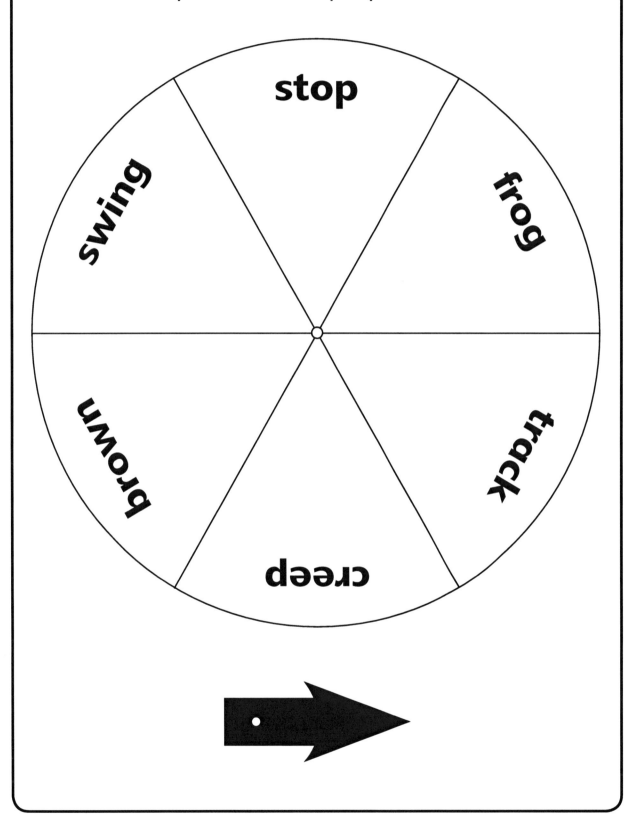

Super sentences

Objectives

To practise previously learned graphemes. To recognise, learn and spell CVC, CVCC and CCVC words. To practise spelling high frequency words and writing sentences.

Background knowledge

At this stage of learning, the children are beginning to develop fluency in recognising and using the 42 phonemes they have learned. They are beginning to be able to spell a range of high frequency words, both decodable and tricky and they can use various strategies to have a go at spelling rhyming and other words, using visual clues such as recognising word families and letter string patterns and applying their knowledge of grapheme-phoneme correspondences.

The activities in this section provide them with opportunities to use the knowledge and strategies available to them in order to spell increasingly complex words including those with adjacent consonants such as *train*.

Activities

● **Photocopiable page 67 'Clippety-clop'**
Practise saying the rhyme together several times. Have fun making up actions to go with it. Hand out the photocopiable sheet and draw the children's attention to the rhyming words. Can they see any patterns of letters? Help them to complete the activity.

● **Photocopiable page 68 'Make it right'**
Introduce this activity with a cuddly toy that keeps getting his words mixed up. Play some games, making the toy say things slightly wrongly – for example, *Pass me the 'ben'* instead of *pen*. Ask the children to help the toy by slowly 'sound talking' the words for him to copy. Use the photocopiable sheet with small groups and work together to spot the misspellings and put them right.

● **Photocopiable pages 69 and 70 'Fill the gaps'**
In these activities the children will have picture clues to help them find the missing words. Make sure that they have identified the missing word correctly and then work with small groups, 'sound talking' each word before they try to spell it. For a plenary session write out the missing words in phoneme frames with the children's help.

● **Photocopiable page 71 'Tramp, tramp, tramp'**
Say the rhyme and practise marching to it. Work with a group of children to complete the photocopiable sheet. Sit in a circle, and take turns to make up a sentence using one of the rhyming words. Help the children to choose a sentence to write out. Provide help as required and make use of phoneme frames to break words up into phonemes in order to spell them.

● **Photocopiable pages 72 and 73 'High frequency words'**
Use these flashcards to help the children learn to spell the decodable and tricky high frequency words expected of them during Phase Four of *Letters and Sounds*. Ideas include making two sets of cards to play snap with and matching the words on the cards to those on photocopiable sheet.

Further ideas

● **Clapping game:** Play a circle game where the children have to clap the rhythm of some two-syllable words. In the centre of the circle, place some magnetic letters, a whiteboard and two-syllable word cards that are made from two words, such as *desktop*, *lunchbox*, *starlight*, *driftwood* and so on. The children pick a word from the centre for everyone to clap before individuals take turns to find the magnetic letters to add to a whiteboard to spell the word.

What's on the CD-ROM

On the CD-ROM you will find:
● Printable versions of all seven photocopiable pages.
● Answers to 'Clippety-clop', 'Make it right', 'Fill in the gaps (1) and (2)' and 'Tramp, tramp, tramp'.
● Interactive versions of 'Make it right' and 'Fill in the gaps (1) and (2)'.

Super sentences

Clippety-clop

■ Say the rhyme. Underline all the words that rhyme with **clop**.

■ Write them in the box. Add some of your own.

Clippety-clop

Clippety-clop, clippety-clop,

Ride the horse, then make him stop.

STOP!

Chippety-chop, chippety-chop,

Lift an axe, then let it drop.

CHOP! CHOP!

Slippety-slop, slippety-slop,

Spill the water, and fetch the mop.

MOP! MOP! MOP!   *Sue Palmer*

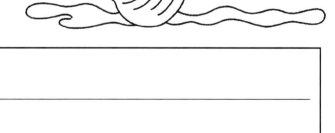

Text © 1999, Sue Palmer; Illustrations © 2009, Cathy Hughes/Beehive Illustration.

Name:

Make it right

■ Check the spelling of the word below. Circle any that do not look right. Write the correct spelling on the line.

■ Then spell some words wrong and ask a partner to spot your mistakes and correct them.

tant		_____
bamd		_____
lamb		_____
nesd		_____
pound		_____
toest		_____
mulk		_____

Super sentences

Fill the gaps (1)

■ Fill in the gaps in the sentences. Use the picture clues to help you.

1. I like camping

in my _____ .

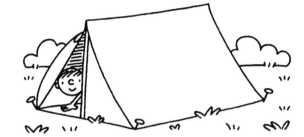

2. The baby bird fell

out of its _____ .

3. There are three ducks

swimming on the _____ .

4. I like _____ with jam on it.

5. I bought some _____

and bread at the shop.

Illustrations © 2009, Cathy Hughes/Beehive Illustration.

SCHOLASTIC
www.scholastic.co.uk   **PHOTOCOPIABLE**   Scholastic Literacy Skills
Spelling: Years 1 and 2   **69**

Name:

Super sentences

Fill the gaps (2)

■ Fill in the gaps in the sentences. Use the picture clues to help you.

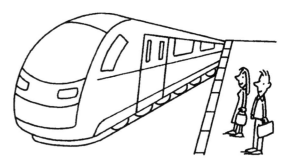

1. The _____

was waiting at platform.

2. I found the _____

next to the pond.

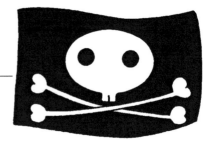

3. The pirate ship had a _____

with a skull and crossbones on it.

4. The _____ at

the circus was really funny.

5. I like to play on my _____

in the garden.

Super sentences

Tramp, tramp, tramp

■ Underline all the words that rhyme with **tramp**.
Make a list of these words in the box.

Tramp, tramp, tramp
(A marching song)

Tramp, tramp, tramp –

We're marching to the camp,

Holding up the lamp,

Tramp, tramp, tramp.

Stamp, stamp, stamp –

It's very cold and damp,

I think I've got the cramp,

Stamp, stamp, stamp.

Tramp, tramp, tramp –

We've made it to the camp!

Here's the marching champ!

Champ, champ, champ! *Sue Palmer*

Text © 1999, Sue Palmer; Illustrations © 2009, Cathy Hughes/Beehive Illustration.

Super sentences

High frequency words (1)

■ Cut out these flashcards and use them for a variety
of games.

went	**it's**
from	**children**
just	**help**
said	**have**
like	**so**

Super sentences

High frequency words (2)

■ Cut out these flashcards and use them for a variety of games.

do	**some**
come	**were**
there	**little**
one	**when**
out	**what**

Assessment

Assessment grid

The following grid shows the main objectives and activities covered in this chapter. You can use the grid to locate activities that cover a particular focus that you are keen to monitor.

Objective	Page	Activity title
To practise previously learned graphemes.	61	Rhyming partners
	64	Spin a letter
	68	Make it right
	69	Fill the gaps (1)
	70	Fill the gaps (2)
To recognise, learn and spell CVC, CVCC and CCVC words.	61	Rhyming partners
	62	Add a letter (1)
	63	Add a letter (2)
	65	Word family spinner
	67	Clippety-clop
	68	Make it right
	69	Fill the gaps (1)
	70	Fill the gaps (2)
	71	Tramp, tramp, tramp
To practise spelling high frequency words.	72	High frequency words (1)
	73	High frequency words (2)
To write sentences.	62	Add a letter (1)
	63	Add a letter (2)
	67	Clippety-clop
	68	Tramp, tramp, tramp

Observation and record keeping

It is difficult to sufficiently monitor children when they are taking part in group activities. Individual assessments need to be done on a regular basis to check the children's knowledge of letters and their ability to segment words for spelling. By this stage, the children will be beginning to have better pencil control and most will be able to form the letters correctly during handwriting activities.

When concentrating on spelling it may still be useful to allow the children to manipulate magnetic letters or cards so that they are focused on the content rather than the process of their writing.

Assessment activity

● **What you need**
Photocopiable page 75 'Making pairs', writing materials, scissors and small pieces of card.

● **What to do**
Work with individual children. Ask a child to look at the pictures, 'sound talk' and then say the words that go with each picture. Encourage them to write the word that corresponds to each picture. Next, ask them to cut out the cards and then find the pair of cards that rhyme. Then challenge them to think of a word that rhymes with each of the other words. Invite them to write the rhyming word onto separate pieces of card and match them together.

Differentiation

● Support less confident children by 'sound talking' a rhyming word and asking them to say what it is. Encourage them to have a go at spelling the words.
● Encourage more confident children to make up more than one rhyme for each card.

Further learning

● **Name rhymes:** Encourage the children to think of a word that rhymes with their name, or the name of one of their friends.
● **Word bank:** Make word banks of rhyming CVC, CCVC and CVCC words together.

Assessment

Making pairs

- Make labels for these pictures.
- Match the pair that rhymes. Make up rhymes for those that do not have a partner.

Illustrations © 2009, Cathy Hughes/Beehive Illustration.

Chapter 5

New grapheme representations

Introduction

In this chapter you will find activities that correspond to Phase Five of *Letters and Sounds*. The children will learn new graphemes and the alternative pronunciations of these. They will begin to appreciate that a phoneme may be represented in several different ways. The ideas in this chapter will help them to learn the common spellings of phonemes and through practice, and as their word recognition and recall skills develop, they will begin to build word-specific knowledge of the spellings of words. They will also start to build up knowledge of 'word families' (words with common letter strings).

Poster notes

Alternative spellings for phonemes (page 77)
The poster for this chapter provides a table of the alternative spellings and example words for the long vowel phonemes /ai/, /ee/, /igh/, /oa/, /oo/. It can be displayed as a useful at-a-glance reference tool and can be used alongside the activities in this chapter. Make sure that the children know how to pronounce the different sounds and ask them to think of words that belong to each set. Which spelling pattern does their word follow? Encourage the children to refer to it and use it to check their own writing and spelling work.

In this chapter

Splitting up page 78	To learn about alternative spellings for phonemes. To practise spelling words with a split digraph. To practise spelling words with adjacent consonants.
Getting longer page 83	To practise spelling words with adjacent consonants. To practise spelling polysyllabic words. To practise writing sentences.
All kinds of ways page 88	To learn and practise using alternative spellings for phonemes.
Frequently used page 93	To learn and practise using alternative spellings for phonemes and to practise spelling high frequency words.
Assessment page 98	Activities and ideas to assess understanding of long vowel sounds.

Alternative spellings for phonemes

/ai/	/ee/	/igh/	/oa/	/oo/	/oo/
ay play	ea peach	y spy	ow slow	ue true	ue cue
a–e make	e–e Steve	ie pie	oe toe	ew blew	ew stew
eigh sleigh	ie thief	i–e time	o–e home	u–e flute	u–e cube
ey they	y pony	i bicycle	o go	ou route	
ei rein	ey key	igh sigh	oa goat	ui suit	
a baby	e me			oe shoe	
ai rain	ee tree			oo zoo	

Splitting up

Objectives

To learn about alternative spellings for phonemes. To practise spelling words with a split digraph. To practise spelling words with adjacent consonants.

Background knowledge

Through a series of rhyming and cloze activities and mnemonics, such as *The e on the end makes O say O*, the children will learn new grapheme-phoneme correspondences involving split digraphs such as 'i–e' and alternative spellings for phonemes (such as 'o–e' for /oa/). In the final activity in this section the children will familiarise themselves with some common spelling patterns involving adjacent consonants such as 'and' and 'est'. All the activities in this section focus on teaching general rules and patterns that will enable the children to generate further words and therefore increase their spelling repertoires.

Activities

● **Photocopiable page 79 'The e on the end'**
Look at the poster together and find the 'a–e', 'i–e', 'o–e' and 'u–e' words. Draw the children's attention to how the first vowel 'says its own name' when there is an 'e' at the end of the word (discuss how the 'u' may also make an /oo/ sound). Look at the pictures on the photocopiable sheet and say the words out loud. Discuss how the words might be spelled before the children fill in the answers.

● **Photocopiable page 80 'All day long!'**
Enlarge the photocopiable sheet and complete it with a group of children. Once complete, say the rhyme again slowly and ask the children to listen for the words that rhyme, challenging them to write them out on individual whiteboards as they hear them.

● **Photocopiable page 81 'Date, gate, plate'**
Help the children to work out what the missing letters on the photocopiable sheet are. Ask them to think of a rhyming word for each one. Discuss the children's ideas: do all their rhyming words follow the same spelling pattern? What other ways have the children found of spelling the same sound? Look at the poster for further ideas. Then ask them to complete the sentences below and make up some of their own.

● **Photocopiable page 82 'Hand in hand'**
Enlarge the photocopiable sheet and read the rhyme together with the children. Ask them to listen out for the rhyming words and invite volunteers to underline the words that rhyme. What do the children notice about the rhyming words? Draw their attention to the common word endings. Provide each child with the photocopiable sheet and discuss what they need to do to complete it.

Further ideas

● **Rhyming strings:** Use a rhyming dictionary to find other groups of rhyming words. Look at any common spelling patterns.
● **Pick a phoneme:** Choose a phoneme that has several different grapheme correspondences (such as /ai/). Check out the different spellings using the poster. Together, make a list of words that contain that phoneme. Cut up the words and divide them into different groups based on their spellings (such as *rain*, *wait* and *train*; *lane*, *snake* and *mate*; *day*, *play* and *tray* and so on). Add to the list over time and decide which are common spellings and which are rarer.

What's on the CD-ROM

On the CD-ROM you will find:
● Printable versions of all four photocopiable pages.
● Answers to 'The e on the end', 'Date, gate, plate' and 'Hand in hand'.
● Interactive versions of 'The e on the end', 'Date, gate, plate' and 'Hand in hand'.

Splitting up

The e on the end

■ The pictures are all clues to words spelled with **a–e**, **i–e**, **o–e** or **u–e**. Work out what each word is and write it in the correct box.

■ Can you write any more words in the boxes?

a–e	i–e	o–e	u–e

Illustrations © 2009, Cathy Hughes/Beehive Illustration.

Splitting up

All day long!

- Use the words to fill in the gaps in the verses in this song.

date	gate	plate	cake	make	take

1. The **e** on the end makes name, same, game

———————— , ———————— , ————————

———————— , ———————— , ————————

The **e** on the end makes **A** say **A**, all day long!

like	bike	strike	wipe	ripe	pipe

2. The **e** on the end makes mine, fine, nine,

———————— , ———————— , ————————

———————— , ———————— , ————————

The **e** on the end makes **I** say **I**, all day long!

nose	close	those	hole	pole	mole

3. The **e** on the end makes bone, cone, stone

———————— , ———————— , ————————

———————— , ———————— , ————————

The **e** on the end makes **O** say **O**, all day long!

Splitting up

Date, gate, plate

■ Fill in the missing letters to make the words. Write a word that rhymes under each one.

| sn __ k __ | sp __ d __ | c __ v __ | n __ m __ | c __ m __ |

_____ _____ _____ _____ _____

■ Use the words you have made to finish these sentences. Then make up some sentences of your own using some words that rhyme.

1. This is a _____ .

2. What is in the _____ ?

3. Jess _____ to school in a car.

4. Anna can write her _____ .

5. Lee has a bucket and _____ .

Illustrations © 2009, Cathy Hughes/Beehive Illustration.

Name:

Splitting up

Hand in hand

- Underline all the **and** words in the rhyme.

Hand in hand

Here we stand,

Hand in hand.

We're the sea,

And we're the land.

We're the waves,

And we're the sand.

Hand in hand,

And hand in hand.

Sue Palmer

- Add the missing **est** words to the sentences below.

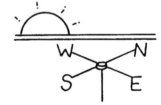

1. The sun sets in the _____ .

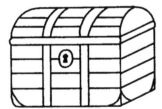

2. There is gold in the _____ .

3. Ben has got a new _____ .

4. My dog is my _____ friend.

SCHOLASTIC
www.scholastic.co.uk

Text © 1999 Sue Palmer; Illustrations © 2009, Cathy Hughes/Beehive Illustration.

Getting longer

To practise spelling words with adjacent consonants. To practise spelling polysyllabic words. To practise writing sentences.

Background knowledge

The children should now be becoming more adventurous in the words that they attempt to spell – they have a secure grasp of the 44 phonemes and are beginning to understand that the phonemes have more than one spelling variation, but that some are more common than others. In these activities they will be looking at common spelling patterns and using them to generate sets of words. They will learn about words that are made up of more than one word (compound words) and generate and spell some of their own. They will also have opportunities to use their spelling skills to write simple sentences that enable them to practise the newly learned grapheme-phoneme correspondences.

Activities

● **Photocopiable page 84 'Keep away!'**
Enlarge the photocopiable sheet and read it aloud to the children. Read it a second time and invite volunteers to underline the sets of 'ink', 'ank' and 'unk' words, using a different colour for each rhyming set. Next, ask the children to write down other words that follow the same pattern on individual whiteboards. Let the children each complete a copy of the photocopiable sheet.

● **Photocopiable page 85 'Two for one'**
Explain how many words that we use are two separate words that have been joined together. Provide some examples such as *lighthouse*, *bathtub* and *footstep*. Give each child the photocopiable sheet and ask them to draw arrows between the words that can be joined together to make new words.

● **Photocopiable page 86 'ack and ick'**
Talk about the sound that 'ck' makes. Explain that common spelling patterns that feature the 'ck' grapheme include words ending in 'ack' and 'ick'.

Complete the photocopiable sheet in a group and challenge the children to work with a partner to think of some 'ick' words.

● **Photocopiable page 87 'Making sentences'**
The pictures provided on the photocopiable sheet are good starting points for focusing on spelling accurately within simple sentences. The pictures encourage the children to use some of the new spelling variations for the long vowel phonemes that they are learning, such as *snake*, *spade*, *seaside* and *sheep*.

Further ideas

● **Sound sentences:** Invite the children to read their sentences from page 87 in 'sound talk', sounding out each phoneme. Suggest that they check their spellings after they have done this. Do they want to change anything?

● **Word banks:** Make a class list of all the compound words that you can think of and that you come across in the stories that you share.

 What's on the CD-ROM

On the CD-ROM you will find:
● Printable versions of all four photocopiable pages.
● Answers to 'Keep away!', 'Two for one' and 'ack and ick'.
● Interactive versions of 'Keep away!' and 'Two for one'.

Name:

Keep away!

■ Underline all the **ink**, **ank** and **unk** words in the rhyme. Use a different colour for each rhyming set.

Keep away!

Big bad Pirate Frank

Likes to walk about and swank,

Wants to make you walk the plank...

Keep away from Pirate Frank!

Funny little Mrs Twink

Mixes something pink to drink –

Says that it will make you shrink...

Keep away from Mrs Twink!

Silly Kelly Elephunk

Lifts up boxes in her trunk,

Then she drops them – clunk, clunk, clunk!

Keep away from Elephunks!

Sue Palmer

Text © 1999, Sue Palmer; Illustrations © 2009, Cathy Hughes/Beehive Illustration.

■ SCHOLASTIC
www.scholastic.co.uk

Getting longer

Two for one

■ Draw lines between words that can be joined together to make new words. The first one has been done for you.

■ Write a list of the words you have made. Can you think of any other words that are made of two words?

sand	wood
wind	pit
bean	stand
hand	mill
lunch	box
tree	light
drift	stalk
star	top

Name:

Getting longer

ack and ick

■ Fill in the missing words in these sentences.
Clue: They all end with **ack**.

1. We have a _____ at break.

2. The car left a _____ in the mud.

3. A _____ is like a hut.

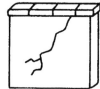

4. There is a _____ in the wall.

5. We jumped on the hay _____.

6. A zebra has _____ and white stripes.

■ Can you think of some words that rhyme with **stick**? Write them down here.

_____

_____

Illustrations © 2009, Cathy Hughes/Beehive Illustration.

Name:

Making sentences

■ Make up a sentence to go with each picture.

Illustrations © 2009, Cathy Hughes/Beehive Illustration.

SCHOLASTIC
www.scholastic.co.uk   **PHOTOCOPIABLE**   Scholastic Literacy Skills
Spelling: Years 1 and 2   **87**

All kinds of ways

Objective

To learn and practise using alternative spellings for phonemes.

Background knowledge

The English language is a hard one to master. There are so many variations and exceptions to common patterns that have to be learned and applied. One of the hardest things to grasp is that the same phoneme can be spelled in a number of different ways, although some are more common than others.

In these activities the children will be exploring some of the most common spellings for some of the long vowel phonemes. At this stage it may be useful to introduce some general rules that help the children to remember the most common forms, such as that the phoneme /ai/ is commonly represented by 'ai' in the middle of words and 'ay' at the ends of words.

Activities

● **Photocopiable page 89 'ee or ea?'**
Make sure that the children are clear about the pronunciation of 'ee' and 'ea' and they understand that they represent the same sound (/ee/). Enlarge the photocopiable sheet and identify the pictures. Invite the children to use individual whiteboards to write down what they think the correct spellings are. Discuss the children's answers.

● **Photocopiable page 90 'Rain and play'**
Make sure that the children are clear about the pronunciation of 'ai' and 'ay' and they understand that they represent the same sound (/ai/). Explain that as a general rule the phoneme /ai/ is commonly represented by 'ai' in the middle of words and 'ay' at the ends of words. Let the children complete their own photocopiable sheet and discuss the answers. Does the general rule hold for these words?

● **Photocopiable page 91 'The great big goat'**
Make sure that the children are clear about the pronunciation of 'oa' and 'ow' and they understand that they represent the same sound (/oa/). Explain that as a general rule the phoneme /oa/ is commonly represented by 'oa' in the middle of words and 'ow' at the ends of words. Let the children complete their own photocopiable sheet and discuss the answers. Does the general rule hold for these words?

● **Photocopiable page 92 'The Crazy Zoo'**
Enlarge the photocopiable sheet and invite volunteers to come and underline the different spelling variations for the phoneme /oo/, using different colours. Discuss how all the words underlined rhyme because they all finish with the same sound, even though it is spelled in a variety of ways. Fill in the boxes with the different sets of words and display these lists in your writing area for future reference.

Further ideas

● **Make a poster:** Make your own poster showing the different spelling variations for the phonemes. Follow the format of the poster on page 77, but add extra columns for other phonemes. As well as providing example words for each spelling variation, encourage the children to draw helpful pictures when appropriate. This poster can be constantly added to and will make excellent reference material.

 What's on the CD-ROM

On the CD-ROM you will find:
● Printable versions of all four photocopiable pages.
● Answers to all four photocopiable pages.
● Interactive versions of 'ee or ea' and 'The great big goat'.

All kinds of ways

ee or ea?

■ The pictures are all clues to **ee** or **ea** words. Work out what each word is. Is it **ee** or **ea**? Write it in the correct box.

ee	**ea**

Name:

All kinds of ways

Rain and play

■ Fill in the missing gaps in these sentences. Use an **ai** or **ay** word.

1. Cows eat

_____ .

2. This rat has a

long _____ .

3. The _____

left a _____ .

■ Look at the pictures. Decide if they are **ay** or **ai** words. Write the words in the correct boxes.

ay	ai

PHOTOCOPIABLE   **SCHOLASTIC**
www.scholastic.co.uk

All kinds of ways

The great big goat

■ Say the rhyme together. Underline all the **oa** words in one colour and the **ow** words in another colour.

The great big goat and the tiny little crow

Grey-beard Billy is a great big goat

With great big buckles on his hat and coat.

He lives in a castle with a great big moat

And he floats all around it in a great big boat.

Tiddy-wee Tilly is a tiny little crow –

She wears a hat with a tiny little bow.

And she follows in a yacht so tiny and low

That Grey-beard Billy doesn't even know!

Sue Palmer

■ Finish these sentences with **oa** or **ow** words.

1. I _____ the ball to my friend.

2. Joe likes _____ for breakfast.

3. Dan will _____ out the candles.

Text © 1999, Sue Palmer; Illustrations © 2009, Cathy Hughes/Beehive Illustration.

Name:

The Crazy Zoo

■ Say this rhyme together. Underline the **oo** words in one colour, the **ue** words in another colour and the **ew** words in another colour.

Boo, Sue and Drew

In the Crazy Zoo, there's a cow called Boo,

And she won't eat grass and she won't say moo,

But she jumps around and she shouts, 'Yoohoo!'

And she thinks that she is a kangaroo.

In the Crazy Zoo there's a cat called Sue,

And she sticks pink stars on her back with glue,

And she won't drink milk but I've heard it's true

That she eats brown bread if the crusts are blue.

In the Crazy Zoo there's a dog called Drew,

And all his life he's had bones to chew

And bowls and bowls of delicious stew,

So Drew just grew and grew and grew.

Sue Palmer

■ Fill the boxes with words from the rhyme.

oo	ue	ew

Text © 1999, Sue Palmer; Illustrations © 2009, Cathy Hughes/Beehive Illustration.

Frequently used

Objectives

To learn and practise using alternative spellings for phonemes. To practise spelling high frequency words.

Background knowledge

The activities in this section continue to explore the different spelling variations that exist for the same phoneme – in this instance the /igh/ phoneme with its common spelling patterns of 'igh', 'y' and ie'. In addition this section provides flashcards of the additional high frequency words that the children are expected to be able to read and spell during Phase Five of the *Letters and Sounds* programme. Many of the high frequency words that the children will be expected to know at this stage follow regular and predictable patterns, or use spelling variations that the children will have come across during their phonics sessions. Some of the words, however, are trickier and tend to be irregular in their spelling pattern or use phoneme-grapheme correspondences that are infrequent or have not yet been learned by the children. The activities below will help the children to learn and practise these essential words.

Activities

● **Photocopiable page 94 'y, igh or ie?'**
Make sure that the children are clear about the pronunciation of 'igh', 'ie' and 'y' and that they understand that they represent the same sound (/igh/) in this instance. Before you look at the photocopiable sheet, ask the children to think of as many words as they can that make the /igh/ sound. Write them down on the board and then ask individuals to come and underline words in the same colour that follows the same spelling pattern. Enlarge the photocopiable sheet and complete it together. Finish by inviting the children to use individual whiteboards and pens to make up and write down a sentence of their own using one of the words.

● **Photocopiable pages 95, 96 and 97 'High frequency words'**
Use these handy flashcards in a number of ways – for games of snap (make two copies of the cards); for rapid recall – showing the words in quick succession for the children to read out; for sorting activities (sorting by initial sounds, spelling patterns, vowel sounds, number of letters) and so on. Learning the tricky words on photocopiable page 97 (and *oh* from photocopiable page 96) requires more intensive teaching. Start by explaining that *Mr* and *Mrs* are shortened versions of the words *Mister* and *Mistress*. Then use a series of dots and lines underneath the words printed on the flashcards (where a dot denotes a single grapheme-phoneme correspondence and a line denotes a phoneme represented by more than one grapheme). Talk about the bits of the words that don't follow the usual spelling pattern for the sound or are tricky in some way. 'Sound talk' and blend the words before covering them up and then writing them on individual whiteboards to check.

Further ideas

● **Post boxes:** Provide post-boxes with labels showing each of the long vowel phonemes. Write out several words on cards that contain these phonemes (using a variety of spelling variations). Encourage the children to read the words on the cards and decide which post boxes they will post them into.

 What's on the CD-ROM

On the CD-ROM you will find:
● Printable versions of all four photocopiable pages.
● Answers to 'y, igh or ie?'.
● Interactive version of 'y, igh or ie?'.

Name:

y, igh or ie?

■ Look at the pictures and decide whether they are **ie**, **igh** or **y** words. Write the words in the correct boxes.

ie	igh	y

■ Finish these sentences.

1. Pigs live in a _____ .

2. The _____ rode a horse.

3. The washing is hanging out to _____ .

Frequently used

High frequency words (1)

don't	**old**
I'm	**by**
time	**house**
about	**your**

Frequently used

High frequency words (2)

day	made
came	make
here	saw
very	oh

Frequently used

High frequency words (3)

their	people
Mr	Mrs
looked	called
asked	could

Assessment

Assessment grid

The following grid shows the main objectives and activities covered in this chapter. You can use the grid to locate activities that cover a particular focus that you are keen to monitor.

Objective	Page	Activity title
To learn about alternative spellings for phonemes.	79 80 81	The e on the end All day long! Date, gate, plate
To practise spelling words with a split digraph.	79 80 81	The e on the end All day long! Date, gate, plate
To practise spelling words with adjacent consonants.	82 84 86	Hand in hand Keep away! ack and ick
To practise spelling polysyllabic words.	85	Two for one
To practise writing sentences.	81 82 87	Date, gate, plate Hand in hand Making sentences
To learn and practise using alternative spellings for phonemes.	89 90 91 92 94	ee or ea? Rain and play The great big goat The crazy zoo y, igh or ie?
To practise spelling high frequency words.	95 96 97	High frequency words (1), (2) and (3)

Observation and record keeping

It is difficult to sufficiently monitor children when they are taking part in group activities. Individual assessments need to be done on a regular basis to check the children's knowledge of letters and their ability to segment words for spelling.

At this stage the children will be learning that a phoneme may be represented in more than one way. They need plenty of opportunities to identify the different ways to spell the same sound. Work on word families and rhyming games will reinforce this knowledge and through experience they can be helped to appreciate that some spelling patterns are more common than others. At this stage they are expected to know the most common variations for spelling a phoneme, with an awareness of some of the other ways. Keep a checklist of the variations that you have introduced to the children; this will help you to keep track of individual children's progress. Set assessment activities (such as the one on page 99) that monitor the children's grasp of these new spelling variations. You will also need to assess the children's ability to spell the 100 high frequency words (see the Appendices of *Letters and Sounds*).

Assessment activity

● **What you need**
Photocopiable page 99 'Sort the cards', scissors, pencils and colouring pencils.
● **What to do**
Ask the children to cut out the cards and say each corresponding word to you. Ask them to listen carefully to the long vowel sound in each word. Challenge them to sort the cards into pairs of words that have the same long vowel sound (they may not necessarily rhyme). Invite the children to have a go at spelling the word on the back of the card.

Differentiation

● Remind less confident learners that the same sound may be represented in more than one way. Allow them to refer to your poster and other reference materials to check their spellings.
● Challenge more confident learners to find examples that show three different ways to spell each phoneme.

Further learning

● **Phoneme spotter:** Read the children a 'phoneme spotter' story such as the ones found in Phase Five of *Letters and Sounds*. Ask them to listen out for a specific phoneme such as /ee/. Make a list of all the words that contain your chosen phoneme. Discuss the variations.

Assessment

Sort the cards

■ Cut out the cards and say the words. All the words have a long vowel sound. Sort them into groups.

Illustrations © 2009, Cathy Hughes/Beehive Illustration.

Chapter 6
Affixes

Introduction

In this chapter you will find activities that correspond to Phase Six of *Letters and Sounds*. At this stage, children will be spelling words in a phonemically accurate way, and although they may use unconventional spellings from time to time they will be beginning to accumulate more word-specific knowledge. During this stage children need to learn how to add suffixes and prefixes to words; they also need to have an understanding of tense and grammar as this will inform their spelling choices (for example that '-ed' is the regular past tense ending; so the past tense of *jump* is written as *jumped* and not *jumpt*).

In this chapter

Poster notes

Yesterday, today and tomorrow (page 101)
The poster for this chapter provides six pictures showing a child doing a range of things, as well as three flashcards with the words *Yesterday*, *Today* and *Tomorrow*. The cards can be cut out, or simply pointed to. The pictures are to be used as the basis for learning the concept of past, present and future tenses; the children must say and/or write sentences starting with one of the words on the flashcards (specified by a teacher), altering the tense as appropriate. They provide useful discussion points for exploring regular and irregular suffixes and spellings.

Affixes

Yesterday, today and tomorrow

Illustrations © 2009, Cathy Hughes/Beehive Illustration.

In the past

Objective

To learn about the past tense. To investigate and learn how to add suffixes.

Background knowledge

At this stage it is important that the children see the links between spelling and grammar – for example, an understanding of past and present tense will help children to make spelling choices (such as knowing the common suffixes to add). The first two activities in this section support an understanding of tense and help children to recognise and learn common spelling patterns as well as being aware of the exceptions. In the 'Five or six?' activity, the children will appreciate that the suffix '-ed' can be pronounced in two different ways. And in 'Investigating "-ing"', the children will explore the ways in which a suffix affects both meaning and spelling and they will be encouraged to identify patterns and make generalised spelling rules.

Activities

● **Photocopiable page 103 'In the past'**
Before you begin, have some fun making up sentences for the pictures on poster page 101 'Yesterday, today and tomorrow'. Explore different tenses and ensure that the children understand the difference between past, present and future. Enlarge the photocopiable sheet and start by identifying the verbs together. Invite volunteers to change the verbs to the past tense and agree the answers together. Let the children have a go at writing the words and then come back together to discuss any patterns.

● **Photocopiable page 104 'Today and yesterday'**
Check understanding of the concept of today and yesterday by using poster page 101 'Yesterday, today and tomorrow' to make up some sentences. Do some 'word sums' orally before giving each child a photocopiable page, making sure that they understand that the suffix '-ed' signifies the past tense of a verb.

● **Photocopiable page 105 'Five or six?'**
This activity will help the children to understand that the suffix '-ed' may be pronounced in two different ways – either as two phonemes /e/d/ (*wanted*) or as one phoneme /t/ (*jumped*). Breaking up the words into phoneme frames will help them to make this distinction.

● **Photocopiable page 106 'Investigating -ing'**
Give each child an individual whiteboard and enlarge the photocopiable sheet. Say the words and ask the children to add '-ing' to each one and to write them on their individual whiteboards. Then, display them for the children and, as a group, look for any patterns. Ask: *What happens if a word ends in 'e'? What if it ends in a single consonant? Which words remain the same?*

Further ideas

● **Tense teaser:** Choose a passage from a favourite story and ask the children to help you change the tense of the verbs.

● **Find the base word:** Provide a list of words that have had the '-ed' suffix added to them and ask the children to give you the base word. For example, the base word of *jumped* is *jump* or *hopped* and *hop*.

What's on the CD-ROM

On the CD-ROM you will find:
● Printable versions of all four photocopiable pages.
● Answers to 'In the past', 'Today and yesterday' and 'Investigating ing'.
● Interactive versions of all four photocopiable pages.

In the past

- Read the short story below. Find the verbs that are in the present tense.
- Read again and change the verbs to the past tense.

I walk to the shops. On the way I spot a bird pecking some seed. It is windy and I notice the flowers blowing in the wind. At the shops I buy some milk and some bread. On the way home I stop at the park and climb a tree.

- Try to spell the past-tense words here. Are there any patterns?

_____

_____

_____

Illustrations © 2009, Cathy Hughes/Beehive Illustration.

Name:

In the past

Today and yesterday

| jump + ed = jumped | dream + ed = dreamed |

■ Write the **-ed** words. Use some of the words to finish the sentences below.

rain + ed = _____	play + ed = _____
frown + ed = _____	milk + ed = _____
float + ed = _____	cook + ed = _____

1. Today is sunny, but yesterday it

_____ .

2. Today I'm at school, but yesterday

we _____ .

3. Now I am smiling, but yesterday I

_____ .

4. Now the boat is sinking, but

yesterday it _____ .

5. Today I'm having a

sandwich, but yesterday Dad

_____ lunch.

Five or six?

■ 'Sound talk' the words below. Cut out the letters and put each sound into the five or six phoneme frame. Show your partner. Do you both agree?

wanted	helped	jumped	rounded

✂

w	a	n	t	e	d
h	e	l	p	ed	j
u	m	r	ou	d	

Name:

Investigating -ing

■ Add **-ing** to the words below. Can you spot any patterns? Sort them into three categories.

hope _____   like _____

hide _____   ride _____

bite _____   jump _____

sing _____   march _____

hop _____   stop _____

run _____   skip _____

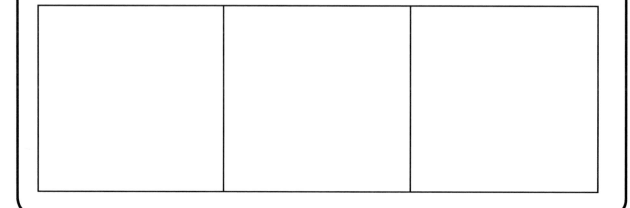

SCHOLASTIC
www.scholastic.co.uk

Illustrations © 2009, Cathy Hughes/Beehive Illustration.

Super suffixes

To investigate and learn how to add suffixes. To investigate how adding suffixes changes words.

Background knowledge

In these activities the children will be learning how to add common suffixes to base words. The children will begin to understand that sometimes the base word may change when a suffix is added. Investigations into spelling patterns, such as in 'Investigating -er' and 'Investigating -ly', will help the children to make general spelling rules that can be applied to the majority of words that fit specific criteria. For example, if a base word ends in a single consonant preceded by a single vowel and the suffix begins with a vowel, double the consonant letter, for example, *red – redder*.

Activities

● **Photocopiable page 108 'Word building'**
For this activity it will help if the children understand the associated grammar. The '-er' suffix is used in two ways here: firstly, it is added to verbs to denote the person doing the action (such as a *teacher*); and secondly, it is added to adjectives to give the comparative word (such as *louder*). Invite the children to think of some of their own examples of adding '-er' to words.

● **Photocopiable page 109 'Investigating -er'**
Enlarge the photocopiable sheet and discuss the words. Provide individual whiteboards and ask volunteers to say the words out loud, asking the children to write the new '-er' word onto their boards. Remind the children that sometimes changes will need to be made to the base words. Compare and check answers and write the correct version on the board. Discuss the final list and decide on categories to sort the words into. Can the children make up any generalised rules for adding '-er'?

● **Photocopiable page 110 'The -y suffix'**
Explain how by adding the '-y' suffix to the words on this page the children are turning nouns into adjectives. Suggest that the children work in pairs to use all the '-y' words on the page to caption the pictures and complete the sentences. Use dictionaries to find some other words to turn from noun to adjective by adding the '-y' suffix.

● **Photocopiable page 111 'Investigating -ly'**
Explain how by adding the '-ly' suffix to the words on this photocopiable sheet, the children are turning adjectives into adverbs. Start by writing up some examples of your own onto the board, such as *cheeky – cheekily*; *joyful – joyfully*; *quick – quickly*. Talk about the words you have made. Have the base words always remained the same? Ask individuals to describe what has happened to them. Let the children work in pairs, then feed back as a class or group and look for spelling patterns and generalisations.

Further ideas

● **Spot the mistake:** Check the children's understanding of the general rules for adding different suffixes to base words. Write lists of words that end with the same suffix onto the whiteboard, occasionally sneaking in a misspelled word. Ask the children to spot your errors and provide the correct spellings.

What's on the CD-ROM

On the CD-ROM you will find:
● Printable versions of all four photocopiable pages.
● Answers to all four photocopiable pages.
● Interactive version of 'Investigating -er'.

Name:

Word building

■ Make the **-er** words. Match the new words to the pictures by drawing arrows.

paint + er =   sing + er =   teach + er =

_____   _____   _____

■ Make these words.

small + er = _____   loud + er = _____

sharp + er = _____   cold + er = _____

■ Use the words to finish the sentences below.

1. This pencil is sharp, but that one is _____ .

2. My brother is small, but the baby is _____ .

3. My voice is loud, but Tim's is _____ .

4. The fridge is cold, but the freezer is _____ .

Illustrations © 2009, Cathy Hughes/Beehive Illustration.

SCHOLASTIC
www.scholastic.co.uk

ating -er

ow. Can you spot any
p   ee categories.

red _____ funny _____

cook _____ run _____

messy _____ teach _____

hot _____ sunny _____

sing _____ flat _____

happy _____ paint _____

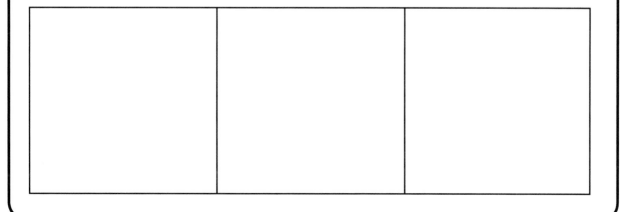

Illustrations © 2009, Cathy Hughes/Beehive Illustration.

Name:

Super suffixes

The -y suffix

- Look at the word sum below.

  rain + y = rainy

- Do the following word sums to make **-y** words.

mess + y = _____   sleep + y = _____

thirst + y = _____   gloom + y = _____

bump + y = _____   crisp + y = _____

_____ _____ _____

- Finish the sentences using some of the words you have made.

1. The old house was very dark and _____ .

2. We had a _____ ride down the little lane.

3. Sarah likes pizza with a thin _____ base.

Illustrations © 2009, Cathy Hughes/Beehive Illustration.

Investigating -ly

■ Add **-ly** to the words below. Talk to your partner about any patterns you notice and sort them into groups of your choice.

merry _____   happy _____

sad _____   safe _____

rude _____   glad_____

bright _____   bad _____

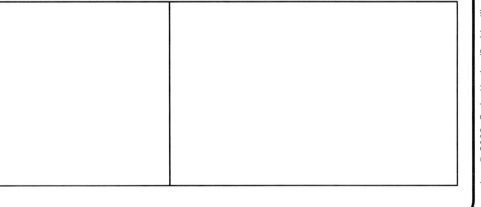

Illustrations © 2009, Cathy Hughes/Beehive Illustration.

All change

Objectives

To investigate and learn how to add suffixes. To investigate how adding suffixes and prefixes changes words.

Background knowledge

In this section we continue to look at adding suffixes to base words, investigating the changes that this makes to their spelling and also to their meaning. We have discovered that an understanding of the grammar being used can help children to realise the spelling patterns and rules that need to be applied, which in turn helps their ability to generate additional and related words. In this section we also introduce the idea of adding prefixes to words. Children will feel empowered to see that they can spell a whole range of new words once they are confident with the base words and know which prefixes can be put with them.

Activities

● **Photocopiable page 113 'The -ful suffix'**
Write a number of suffixes that the children have learned on the board (such as '-er', '-ed', '-ing', '-ly' and so on). Add the suffix '-ful' to the list. Now write a number of random words onto the board – a mixture of nouns, adjectives and verbs. Invite volunteers to come up and make a word sum. Discuss the child's choice and decide together if the base word has changed. Next, find out the words that can have the suffix '-ful' added to them. What sort of words have you made? (Adjectives.) Have any of the base words changed? Now invite pairs to complete the photocopiable sheet together.

● **Photocopiable page 114 'The -less suffix'**
Enlarge the photocopiable sheet and read the word sums together to make the 'new' words. Check that the children understand the meaning of the words. Try to think of some other words that end with the same

suffix, such as *pointless*, *tasteless* and *thoughtless*. Ask the children to work with a partner to make up some sentences using the words from the sheet or words of their own choice. Check the spellings together.

● **Photocopiable page 115 'All done in!'**
Provide the children with dictionaries and ask them to look up words beginning with 'in-'. Suggest they choose five or six to write onto their individual whiteboards. Ask the children to tell you their words and together put them into word sums showing the base word and prefix (such as *in + to = into*). Reinforce the work by asking each child to complete the photocopiable sheet.

● **Photocopiable page 116 'To be or not to be…'**
Start by asking the children to think of as many words as possible that begin with the prefix 'be'. Let them work with a partner and write them on individual whiteboards. Collect the children's words and write a list of them, orally breaking them down into prefix and base word as you write them. Let the children work with their partner to complete the photocopiable sheet.

Further ideas

● **Clap the syllables:** Revise the lists of words that you have spelled using the prefixes and suffixes in this group of activities. Say the word sums, and also clap out the syllables of the words to reinforce their structure.

What's on the CD-ROM

On the CD-ROM you will find:
● Printable versions of all four photocopiable pages.
● Answers to all four photocopiable pages.
● Interactive versions of 'The -ful suffix' and 'All done in'.

All change

The -ful suffix

■ Do the word sums to make **-ful** words.

care + ful = _____   help + ful = _____

use + ful = _____   power + ful = _____

grate + ful = _____   cheer + ful = _____

■ Choose a word above to match each picture.

_____   _____   _____

■ Finish the sentences using some of the words you have made.

1. A tin opener is _____ .

2. Sita was _____ when Mel found her lunchbox.

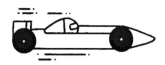

3. The racing car was very _____ .

■SCHOLASTIC   **PHOTOCOPIABLE**   **Scholastic Literacy Skills**
www.scholastic.co.uk   Spelling: Years 1 and 2   **113**

All change

The -less suffix

■ Do the word sums to make **-less** words.

stain + less = _____   help + less = _____

home + less = _____   end + less = _____

■ Finish the sentences using some of the words you have made.

   1. The long road seemed _____ .

   2. Our forks are made of _____ steel.

   3. The sick little puppy was _____ so I

      looked after him.

■ Do these word sums. Use the words you have made to write two or three sentences of your own.

use + less = _____   care + less = _____

hope + less = _____   breath + less = _____

All change

All done in!

■ Do the word sums to make **in-** words.

in + to = _____   in + sect = _____

in + deed = _____   in + vent = _____

in + side = _____   in + dex = _____

■ Write an **in-** word to match each picture.

_____   _____   _____

■ Finish the sentences using some of the words you have made.

1. When he won the cup,
Jack was very pleased _____ .

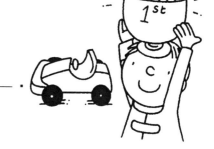

2. It is cold outside, but warm _____ .

3. We cut the cake _____ four slices.

Illustrations © 2009, Cathy Hughes/Beehive Illustration.

Name:

All change

To be or not to be...

■ Do the word sums to make **be-** words.

be + long = _____

be + side = _____

be + witch = _____

be + ware = _____

■ Use the words you have made to finish these sentences.

1. _____ of the dog!

2. Jan was standing _____ two boys.

3. These boots _____ to Alex Brown.

4. Don't let her _____ you!

■ Do these word sums. Use the words to make up some sentences of your own.

be + come = _____   be + fore = _____

be + cause = _____   be + hind = _____

Illustrations © 2009, Cathy Hughes/Beehive Illustration.

The long and the short

To investigate how adding suffixes and prefixes change words. To learn how to spell multi-syllable words. To find and learn the difficult bits in words.

Background knowledge

In this section we continue to look at adding prefixes and suffixes to base words to generate a range of new words. The children will be encouraged to investigate the changes that this makes to the spelling and the meaning of the words. The prefixes and suffixes learned in this section are 'un-' and 're-', '-s' and '-es'. The children will also be helped to analyse and identify the tricky elements of words, contributing to their awareness of general spelling patterns and exceptions and developing their confidence as spellers. In the final activity the children will be taught how to segment words into their constituent syllables. This will help them with the spelling of long and compound words, as it breaks the words into manageable chunks which can be further segmented into phonemes if necessary.

Activities

● **Photocopiable page 118 'Feeling unhappy?'**
Have some fun making some 'before and after' style pictures to go with words that can have the 'un-' prefix added to them. For example, draw some healthy fruit and vegetables on a card with the caption *healthy*; then flip the card over to reveal the word *unhealthy* with a selection of crisps, cakes, sweets and so on. Complete the photocopiable sheet with small groups.

● **Photocopiable page 119 'The re- prefix'**
Write up a list of 're-' words on the board and say them together. Ask the children what they think the prefix 're-' means. Split the words into prefixes and base words. Invite the children to take a close look at the first five words. Cover the words and invite the children to write on individual whiteboards as you say them. Discuss

the children's results. Did it help to break the word into two parts? What other strategies could they use? Give each child the photocopiable sheet to complete.

● **Photocopiable page 120 '-s or -es?'**
Enlarge the photocopiable sheet and say the general rule together. Look at each word in the list, one at a time, and consider whether it should have '-s' or '-es' added to it. Make a few deliberate mistakes for the children to spot. Together, think of some other words that follow this general rule and invite the children to complete the photocopiable sheet.

● **Photocopiable page 121 'Syllables'**
Start with some syllable clapping games, such as clapping the syllables in the children's names, or the names of objects around the room. Give each child the photocopiable sheet to complete and remind them that they are breaking up the words into syllables (not phonemes).

Further ideas

● **Listen carefully:** Make a collection of objects of different numbers of syllables, such as a football, a spoon, a calculator and so on. Explain that you are not going to say the name of the object but you are going to clap the number of syllables. Can the children guess which object you are clapping?

What's on the CD-ROM

On the CD-ROM you will find:
● Printable versions of all four photocopiable pages.
● Answers to all four photocopiable pages.
● Interactive versions of '-s or -es' and 'Syllables'.

Name:

The long and the short

Feeling unhappy?

happy

unhappy

■ Do the word sums to make **un-** words.

un + dress = _____   un + pack = _____

un + fair = _____   un + healthy = _____

un + fold = _____   un + true = _____

■ Use some of these words to label these pictures

_____   _____   _____

Illustrations © 2009, Cathy Hughes/Beehive Illustration.

The long and the short

The re- prefix

■ Do the word sums to make **re-** words.

re + ply = _____   re + turn = _____

re + play = _____

■ Use the words you have made to finish these sentences.

1. I go to school in the morning and I

_____ home at 4 o'clock.

2. If I like a DVD, I _____ it lots

of times.

3. Another word for 'answer' is _____ .

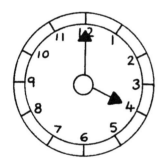

■ Do these word sums to make some more **re-** words.

re + cord = _____   re + peat = _____

re + wind = _____

■ Use the words you have made to write some

sentences.

_____

_____

Illustrations © 2009, Cathy Hughes/Beehive Illustration.

Name:

The long and the short

-s or -es?

It is tricky to remember when to add **-s** or **-es**. Read this spelling pattern rule to help you:

Usually **-s** is simply added to the base word. But for words ending in **s**, **ss**, **ch**, **sh**, **z** and **zz**, and when **y** is replaced by **i**, you use **-es**.

■ Add **-s** or **-es** to the following words. Make two sets and write them in the boxes provided.

-s	-es

stop	circus	night	fuss
park	boat	puppy	buzz
fizz	melt	goal	match

The long and the short

Syllables

■ These words have been divided into syllables. Do the word sums to make the words.

car + pet   = _____   tar + get   = _____

foot + ball = _____   ex + it= _____

hand + bag = _____   gar + den = _____

■ Divide each word into syllables. Write each syllable on a line.

belong   = _____ + _____

today   = _____ + _____

person   = _____ + _____

outside = _____ + _____

under   = _____ + _____

inside   = _____ + _____

■ Use some of the words you have made to finish these sentences.

1. The boat is _____ the bridge.

2. The cat is going _____ .

Illustrations © 2009, Cathy Hughes/Beehive Illustration.

Assessment

The following grid shows the main objectives and activities covered in this chapter. You can use the grid to locate activities that cover a particular focus that you are keen to monitor.

Objective	Page	Activity title
To learn about the past tense.	103 104	In the past Today and yesterday
To investigate and learn how to add suffixes.	105 106 108 110 113 114	Five or six? Investigating -ing Word building The -y suffix The -ful suffix The -less suffix
To investigate how adding suffixes changes words.	108 109 110 111	Word building Investigating -er The -y suffix Investigating -ly
To investigate how adding suffixes and prefixes change words.	109 111 114 115 116 118 119	Investigating -er Investigating -ly The -less suffix All done in! To be or not to be… Feeling unhappy The re- prefix
To learn how to spell multi-syllable words.	105 121	Five or six? Syllables
To find and learn the difficult bits in words.	120	-s or -es?

By now the children will be confident in segmenting words into phonemes to spell them, but it is important that children develop a wider range of strategies to help them to generate words from known

patterns and to begin to know which grapheme to choose when there are several possibilities.

Observations of the choices that children make can feed into plans for areas that need to be revisited. Tricky words need to be learned and part of the skill in doing this is for children to be able to identify the tricky parts of words for themselves (the parts of words that don't conform to general patterns). It is important to spot common and frequently made errors, so that these don't turn into bad habits.

Assessments at this phase will include checking that the children have an understanding of different tenses and grammatical forms – they are unlikely to be able to apply some suffixes, for example if they do not understand when they need to be used.

● **What you need**
Photocopiable page 123 'Touching base', pens or pencils and scissors.
● **What to do**
Check the child's understanding of tense by asking them to give you a sentence for each word, some starting with the word 'yesterday', and others starting with the word 'today'. Now explain that you would like them to turn all the words into the past tense by adding the suffix '-ed'. Once they have made the new words, ask them to cut them out and sort them into groups based on what has happened to the base word. Ask the children to explain their reasons to you.

● Remind less confident learners that the original (or base) word may change when the suffix is added.
● Challenge more confident learners to think of further examples that fit into the categories that they have sorted the words into. Can they also write a spelling rule about adding '-ed' to help others?

● **Tenses:** Provide some word cards showing the present tense of a variety of verbs. Invite the children to add '-ing' and '-ed' to the verbs to make new words. What patterns did they apply? Investigate if the rules are the same for both suffixes.

Assessment

Touching base

■ Add the **-ed** suffix to these base words. Write the new word on the line below each word.

■ Cut out the completed cards. Sort them into groups according to what has happened to the base word. Describe any patterns or exceptions.

wave _____	**bake** _____
marry _____	**hurry** _____
skip _____	**nod** _____
fan _____	**play** _____

General activities

How to use general activities

There are a variety of games and activities in this part of the book, which can be used as generic ways of exploring prefixes, suffixes, word families and tricky words as well as more specific games that take ideas from the book and expand upon them. You may wish to use these activities as part of your spelling routine or during circle time, with the whole class or smaller groups. They are designed to be fast-paced activities used to introduce or assess spellings. The five-minute ideas are intended to be used as fast-paced warm ups or as plenary sessions. They can be used with the whole class or with groups and are flexible enough to be used to focus on your current spelling needs.

Fishing for rhymes

Linked activities:
Chapter 1: page 18
All of Chapter 2

What to do
● Fill your fishing pool (a bucket) with your own choice of rhyming words written onto them. Do not allow the children to see the words before they fish them out.
● Display an enlarged copy of the poem (photocopiable page 127) and read it with the children.
● Discuss why Dan and Emma kept and discarded the words they did.
● Cover the onset letters of *cat* and *hat* to reveal the end-rhyme. Invite suggestions of further rhymes with the same ending.
● Explain that you are going to 'fish' for rhymes together, inviting volunteers to come and pick out two fish cards from the bucket.
● Say the words together and ask the children to decide if they rhyme or not. Let the children take several turns each, until they get a pair!
● Alternatively, play as a pairs-matching game, where children simply turn up the cards as they look for rhyming pairs.

Feely bag phonics

Linked activities:
Chapter 1: page 18
Chapter 2: pages 26, 32

What to do
● Decide on the phoneme, spelling pattern or rhyme that you wish to focus on. Find objects that match your chosen focus (for example: a comb, a cuddly cat, a cake and a car) and place them inside a feely bag.
● Arrange for the group to sit in a circle and start by telling them that all the objects in the bag begin with the same letter/rhyme with *cat,* for example.
● Put your hand in the bag and hold the object. Give the group your clues, for example: *I begin with /k/. You can keep your hair tidy with me. I have lots of teeth. I come in lots of different colours* and so on.
● The child who guesses correctly is passed the bag for them to give clues for another object.
● Place all the objects in the centre of the circle and say the words clearly together. Give older children whiteboards and pens and ask them to have a try at spelling the words.
● Vary the game by using rhyming objects.

Remember me?

Linked activities:
Chapter 2: page 32
Chapter 4: page 60
Chapter 5: page 83

What to do

● This game can be varied to fit in with your current spelling focus and is based on the children's favourite, 'Kim's Game'. You may choose to place objects that all begin with the same letter on the tray, you may prefer to place objects that rhyme on the tray, or alternatively, you may wish to choose a spelling pattern or long vowel sound as the focus.

● Select your objects and place them on a tray. Cover them with a cloth.

● Ask the children to sit in a circle around the tray and uncover it.

● Let the children look at the objects for a moment and then ask them to tell you what is the same about all of them (they may rhyme, they may begin with the same letter and so on).

● Explain that they have got a minute to look at them and memorise the objects before you cover it up.

● Cover the objects and provide each child with a whiteboard and pen. Ask them to write down all the things that they can remember. Remind them of the fact that they all begin with the same letter, or rhyme. This should help them to remember the things.

● Ask each child to pass their whiteboard to a partner to 'mark'. How many has their partner remembered.

● Encourage older children to spell the words accurately and mark each other's work for spelling as well as for how many they remembered.

What's my spelling?

Linked activities:
Chapter 3: page 48
Chapter 4: pages 60, 66

What to do

● Introduce the words or spelling pattern that you have chosen as your focus. Put these words onto flashcards.

● Explain that the children are going to play a game based on the favourite game of 'What's the time Mr Wolf?'.

● Choose one child to be the Wolf who must stand facing the wall. Give a few cards to each of the others, asking them to stand in a row a few metres away from the Wolf.

● In turn, each child takes a small step closer to the Wolf's back. The child calls out *Can you spell…Mr Wolf?* Keeping her back to the others, the Wolf must spell the word that the child calls out.

● The child must check on their card to see if the Wolf is right. If she is, then it's the turn of the next child to take a step closer and ask for a spelling. If the Wolf is wrong, then she swaps roles with the child, who then becomes the new Wolf.

● At any point in the game, the Wolf may spell *d-i-n-n-e-r* instead and chase any of the participating children. If she tags them before they reach the other side of the play area, then they join her as an extra wolf.

● The game continues for a pre-arranged period.

• •

Phonics puppet

● Choose an appealing puppet that will become your phonics puppet. Explain that the children need to help you to teach the puppet how to pronounce things properly, and that sometimes your puppet gets things wrong, so they need to listen carefully. Have a set of phoneme cards (and later words or letter strings) to hand. Hold one up and using the puppet's voice say it either correctly or incorrectly, asking the children to tell the puppet if they have done well, or helping the puppet if they have made a mistake!

Sound table

● Reserve an area of your setting for a phonics or sound table. The table should contain images, objects and activities linked to your current phonics focus. Invite the children to bring in objects for the table that begin with the letter (or rhyme or spelling pattern) that is in focus. Allow the children time to explore the objects as well as having a try at the activity you have placed there (it may be a photocopiable sheet from this book for example). Other ideas include letter stands where a rime such as '-at' is placed on a magnetic board with a selection of other letters that can be added to it ('c', 'h', 'b' and 'r' for example). The children can add the initial sound (or onset) to the rime to make words.

Writing corner

● Stock your writing corner with books and activity sheets that are linked to your current focus. Ideas include a range of mini books, such as *My little book of 'l' words* or lift the flap books where the flap is shaped like a sun and the children have to draw a picture that rhymes with sun (and write the word) underneath the flap.

Word endings

● Write a word ending on the board, such as '-in' and give clues so that the children can guess lots of different '-in' words. For example, *I'm thinking of a sharp shiny object that can be used in sewing* and so on.

Syllable sorting

● Cut multisyllabic word cards into syllable chunks and then mess them up. Challenge children to work with a partner to arrange them back together again. Set time challenges for older and more confident spellers.

Spelling pattern stories

● Have fun making up stories that contain several words with the same long vowel phoneme, such as a story about *Rose the goat*. For example, the story might begin:

Rose was a goat. She had a coat like a goat. She ate oats like a goat. But Rose had a nose that glowed in the dark. That was not like a goat. 'I never chose a nose that glows. I wish I could get rid of it,' moaned Rose. 'I know,' she said. 'I will throw my nose away. 'Rose nodded her head and she tossed her head, but she could not throw her nose away. When the story is finished the children need to identify the many ways in which the same long vowel sound is spelled, underlining them in the story.

Fishing for rhymes

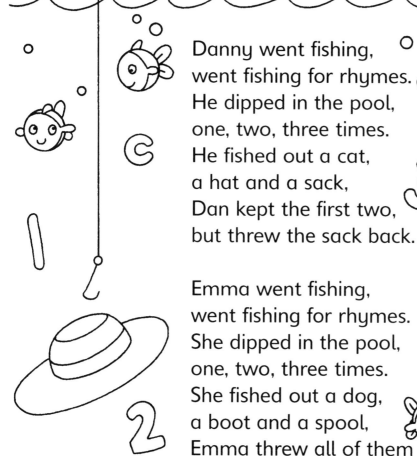

Danny went fishing,
went fishing for rhymes.
He dipped in the pool,
one, two, three times.
He fished out a cat,
a hat and a sack,
Dan kept the first two,
but threw the sack back.

Emma went fishing,
went fishing for rhymes.
She dipped in the pool,
one, two, three times.
She fished out a dog,
a boot and a spool,
Emma threw all of them
back in the pool.

Now you go fishing,
go fishing for rhymes,
You can dip in the pool,
one, two, three times.
Read out your words
to your friends here at school,
And any that don't rhyme,
throw back in the pool.

Celia Warren

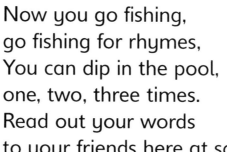

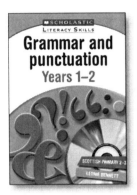
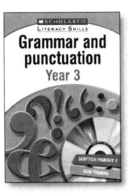

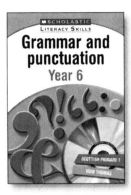
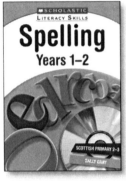
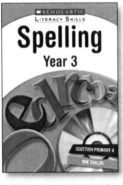
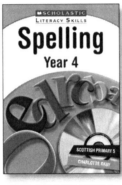
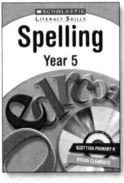

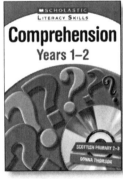
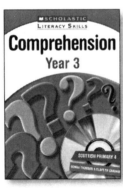
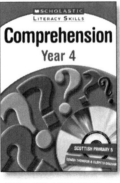

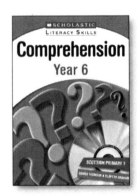